Reiki
Pure and Simple

Elaine Hamilton Grundy

To my mother

Acknowledgements

This book began its germination when I became delightedly pregnant. My brilliant idea was to write a Reiki book during my child's first year. After all, babies sleep for sixteen hours a day don't they? What else would I have to do? Well, here we are, eight years later… a period of gestation considerably longer than I had originally anticipated; but that's how long it *actually* took me to complete this remarkable journey. I have many people to thank for keeping me company along the way, especially my students, who have encouraged and prodded me throughout. You have all taught me so much.

This book would have never, ever been written without the support and brilliance of my editor, Hilary Galea. Thank you for your patience and for keeping me on the path. I also owe a great thank you to all the Reiki practitioners who participated in The Reiki Centre Survey and who shared their wonderful stories and experiences. To Karen Taylor and Nicole Kubbinga for your enthusiastic and unerring support and edits. To Justine Elliott for a masterpiece in design.

I have been fortunate to be surrounded by wonderful, loving people all my life. To my amazing husband, Ian, who supports me no matter what 'weird' thing I am into, you are incredible. To my children, Ella and Holly, who want to be Reiki Masters when they grow up, you inspire me every day. To my dearest mum and dad, who didn't mind me becoming a Reiki Master despite all the tertiary education. To my brothers, Roger and Martin, who simply rock. To my Reiki Masters and mentors, John and Esther Veltheim, thank you for your wisdom. To Rene and Misha Vögtli and Elaine Harris for continuing to inspire me. To Basic Essence, Andrea Yap and Clarice Chan for friendship and fellowship. To Toast Box, Wisma Atria, for the tons of sweet tea, warm service and smiles.

CONTENTS

Introduction

"Ultimately the most important alternative medicine treatment of all … energy medicine."

Dr Mehmet Oz, Cardiovascular Surgeon

This is the story of a too-good-to-be-true therapy: one you can do in your sleep, one that requires no training or effort, one that requires no belief, gift, talent or even desire. Welcome to the wonderful world of Reiki.

Reiki, as a self-healing technique, has a great advantage: it is simple and easy to attain. It is transferred from teacher to student as if the teacher (or Reiki Master) were turning on a switch. Once a student has been attuned to Reiki, the benefits happen automatically through use: simply placing your hands on your body will activate the Reiki and the energy will flow. It is an amazing process.

The primary focus of this book is to introduce the basic principles behind Reiki energy and how Reiki works. It is written for those just beginning their own journey with Reiki and for those who want to deepen their understanding of how Reiki heals.

As its title suggests, this book is about Reiki, pure and simple. It is not about symbols, advanced levels of Reiki or metaphysical aspects of Reiki. There is already a plethora of books sharing a wide variety of techniques and styles of Reiki which can be applied to heal specific illnesses and ailments. Many of these styles combine Reiki energy with other forms of healing, for instance, Jin Shin Jyutsu, Shiatsu or Acupressure, where specific meridian points are used to help ease the flow of energy.

When I was trained, my Reiki Master did not teach any of these techniques (despite the fact that he himself was a gifted acupuncturist and chiropractor by training) and in a sense I feel I was spared! What attracted me to Reiki in the first place was the ease with which treatments were applied – the 'one size fits all' approach was very comforting to me and my novice mind. It is this simple approach that I focus on in later chapters and, in my experience, it has been more than effective in helping me heal all manner of ailments, imbalances and stress in my life.

The aim of this book, therefore, is to open the door for you to find your own path and to strip away, as far as possible, the window dressing. My encouragement to you is the same as I give my students: when reading these pages, keep what rings true for you and throw out the rest. There is no *one* truth, only *your* truth.

Energy healing, which includes Reiki, has yet to become a science. By that I mean we have yet to find definitive answers to how Reiki energy works. What follows is my own truth based on fifteen years of teaching, observing, and experimenting. What is fascinating, especially over the past few decades, is that scientists are also converging on new truths which parallel much of what we teach in Reiki. There seems to be less contradiction and more agreement in the field of holistic and conventional medicine. My hope is that we will continue to see this convergence in theories and, with more unity, a more complete and effective way of taking care of our health and wellness.

Aligned with that is the second focus of this book – the vital role of Reiki for self-healing. Reiki has evolved into an amazing self-help tool and anyone who is not using Reiki to self-heal is, to my mind, missing the point completely. To support the writing of this book and to deepen our understanding of Reiki, The Reiki Centre[1] carried out an international survey, with 546 respondents, which is summarized in this book as an appendix. The key findings were the overwhelming benefits practitioners of Reiki gain when they use Reiki on themselves (what I term 'self-Reiki'). These findings are reported throughout this book as they highlight not only my own experience but the experience of many other Reiki practitioners, ranging from novices to seasoned teachers. Reiki is essentially a self-healing therapy, and this book explores why.

I hope *Reiki, Pure and Simple* helps to widen your scope of reference and gives you some theories that are practical and easy to explain to the people you want to share Reiki with. This book is not only about Reiki, it is about energy in general and how important it is for our energy to be balanced. We start with an exploration of the big picture: Universal Life Energy, and slowly hone our attention down to our body energy and how we can help ourselves to heal and balance. The final chapters look specifically at Reiki techniques and the 'how to' of Reiki. What follows is my own story and interpretation of Reiki energy.

Chapter 1

Elaine's Story

"Stop being so damn stubborn"

My mother

About 17 years ago my mother introduced a very sceptical me to Reiki. At the time I liked to think that I was open-minded – after all, I had travelled the world with my parents, I had had a multi-cultural upbringing courtesy of my Scottish father and Chinese mother and I felt that I was receptive to many different influences. But in reality my mind was closed to anything that I couldn't experience through one or more of my five senses: if I couldn't feel, see, hear, taste or touch it, it didn't exist.

On the flip side, I yearned for connection. My dad is an atheist (ironically from a very Scottish Presbyterian family), my mum brings her own eastern influences and has an ease with Buddhist concepts and the idea of everything being interconnected. When I was young I was very curious about religion, embracing Christianity at the age of ten and taking myself off to Sunday school (much to my father's dismay!); then at university I swung to the polar opposite, becoming a huge fan of Richard Dawkins and seeing the world as purely mechanistic. Over the years I have settled somewhere in the middle, but now I put a huge value on personal experience and much less value on hearsay. In a way, I still rely heavily on my very analytical mind but I am also open to my sixth sense (my intuition) and it has become a very powerful guide for me.

My first experience of Reiki

One day my mum came home from a Reiki course in a very excited state; in fact she was acting like a mad woman! She told me how she had discovered this amazing energy in her hands. All she had to do was put them on my body; the energy would flow through her to me and I would be healed. At first I was having none of it. This Reiki thing was obviously working for mum, but it wasn't going to work for me. It just wasn't my 'thing'. Mum didn't give up however, and eventually I was badgered into letting her Reiki me.

Part of the reason for this turnaround in my thinking was that I had been suffering from sciatica for a while (which was a worry as I was only 25 years old at the time – way too young to be bothered by such ailments!) and realized that it would make sense for me to be open to natural therapies as they might provide some relief rather than relying on pain killers.

At the start of the treatment mum asked me to lie down, and then she gently put her hands on my head. It felt relaxing – but then that's exactly what I would have expected under the circumstances. Then she moved her hands down to my back. Suddenly I started to notice heat. It wasn't just the ordinary heat of someone else's hands, it was *really* hot – as though she was holding an iron over me, or touching me with hot stones. I turned around in surprise, asked her what she was doing and held her hands in mine, but they were a perfectly normal body temperature. After this first treatment I was intrigued, agitated and confused. I certainly hadn't been hit by a thunderbolt that left me believing I could 'learn Reiki and cure the world', but something had happened that I couldn't explain and I needed to understand what it was.

Opening doors with Reiki One

A couple of weeks later I attended a Reiki One course. One of the first processes that takes place during Reiki One is an attunement by the Reiki Master – connecting the students' energy so that Reiki can flow through their hands (see chapter six for more information about Reiki training). For me, the result of this attunement was striking – my hands were hot; they were tingling. After the course I started practising Reiki on myself every day. One of the first things I noticed was that I began sleeping more deeply and easily than before. Ever since I was very young I'd had difficulty going to sleep, and was often awake long after my parents had gone to bed, my mind was so over-active that I just couldn't shut it off. So this new-found ability to deeply sleep was amazing to me. It was as if, all of a sudden, my body just knew how to relax. The resulting rise in my energy levels left me in no doubt that learning Reiki had paid off for me based on this improvement alone.

But gradually, I experienced other benefits from Reiki. I'd always thought that I was a pretty normal, healthy individual – possibly healthier than most. I didn't get sick often and, apart from the sciatica, I didn't have any serious physical ailments. But, in actuality, I was a worrier and carrying a lot of anxiety. For instance, I was scared of the dark and suffered from vertigo; I was claustrophobic and I really hated to be alone. These weren't debilitating issues, but I began to realize that I had allowed them to shape how I lived my life to a certain extent. After I started to practise Reiki I noticed that these fears started to lift. Suddenly I had the freedom to do what *I* wanted to do rather than what *my fears* dictated that I should do. It was incredibly liberating. I noticed other important changes too: I was worrying less, and trusting more.

I was also aware of how different I felt if I didn't practise Reiki: the day just didn't go quite as smoothly without it. At the time I suppose I was burning the candle at both ends. I was working in an advertising agency in Hong Kong and I know that my daily Reiki practise was helping me to keep an important balance within a hectic work environment.

At this stage I had no intention of doing anything more with Reiki. It was giving me everything I needed and was helping me enormously. But about a year and a half after I'd completed Reiki Level One, along came mum again, this time instructing me that I ought to move on to Reiki Level Two.

Reiki Two – my turning point

One of the many ways Reiki Two differs from Reiki One is that the student learns to send energy to a recipient who may not even be in the same country. Although I had overcome my initial scepticism and accepted the obvious benefits of Reiki One this new (to me) concept of 'distance healing' seemed to stretch my credulity one step too far, especially when you bear in mind that this was back in the pre-internet, technological dark ages when the idea of sending any kind of message – let alone healing energy – into the ether was still in its infancy. Yet here I was being asked by my mum to believe that her friend Sue would be able to send Reiki to me – from England to Hong Kong.

After expressing my scepticism I promptly forgot about the conversation until, one afternoon, as I was making my way along the aisles of the supermarket, I felt Reiki all over me. After a year and a half of self-Reiki I knew without a doubt what I was experiencing and looked all around to see who could be responsible, but there was no one near me. With a flash of excitement I suddenly remembered the earlier conversation with my mum. I rushed back home and immediately called Sue. She confirmed that she had indeed been sending me Reiki at the exact moment that I had experienced it. That was all I needed to move on to the next stage. I had my proof.

Becoming a Reiki Master

It was while I was attending the Reiki Two course that I realized teaching Reiki was what I wanted to do. For an analytically-minded person like me, it was my first real taste of intuition. It was simply obvious to me that this was what I needed to do, although at the time I did not imagine it would become a full-time 'job'.

In 1995, over the course of nine months, I trained with a Reiki Master couple, John and Esther Veltheim: a wonderful yin/yang experience. John was a gifted natural therapy practitioner having run a successful chiropractic and acupuncture clinic in Australia, he provided me with so much new information, encouragement and inspiration to experiment, investigate and inquire. Esther was the complete opposite in many ways; a deeply peaceful and beautiful spirit, Esther encouraged me to look inwards to seek my own truth, to listen to my intuition, and to believe in my abilities. I feel truly blessed to have had them both as my mentors.

Much of my Reiki Master training was carried out independently however, without face-to-face contact with my Masters. This proved to be an incredibly intense and introspective period of growth during which I had to determine my own teaching approach and my own philosophy about Reiki.

After qualifying as a Reiki Master, I kept one foot very firmly in the corporate world for many more years. It was important to me to maintain that balance; I enjoyed the dynamics of a high-energy office environment, the intellectual stimulation and challenges of my business career and, on a more practical level, I appreciated the money! Fortunately, I was able to pursue my passion for Reiki in parallel as I had a very generous and open-minded boss who allowed me to hold my Reiki classes in the office. So at weekends I was able to combine my worldly and less-worldly interests in a very practical way as I rearranged the furniture in the conference room to create a Reiki centre for my small groups of students.

As time went on my passion for Reiki grew along with my desire to teach it. In 1997 I moved to Singapore, this time with a market research company. At first, I would hire a function room at a hotel and conduct my Reiki courses from there. But as Reiki became better known and as the word about my courses grew, I aligned myself with a natural health centre where I had the benefit of permanent facilities whenever I needed them.

The Grand Plan was temporarily put on hold at this point with the arrival of babies and a job relocation to the USA for my husband. However, on our arrival back in Singapore several years later, I went straight back to the natural health centre I had been teaching at before our departure and picked up from where I'd left off.

Where I am now

In 2009 I fulfilled a personal dream and opened The Reiki Centre in Singapore so that I could devote myself more fully to Reiki and reach a wider community.

I have noticed two major changes in my Reiki practise since I returned to Singapore: inwardly, becoming a mother has given me a humility and maturity that I had lacked before; outwardly, the level of awareness of Reiki and the open-mindedness of the students attending my courses has increased very noticeably. When, ten years before, I asked students what they hoped to get out of the course, a typical answer would be that they wanted to heal a specific physical ailment or disease. Now the answer is far more likely to be "I want to find the dimension that's missing in my life" or "I want to find myself". The shift in the desire for self-awareness, happiness and fulfilment has really been quite astounding.

My own personal journey with Reiki is far from over; every year brings more peace, more fulfilment and more happiness into my life. In the beginning my healing was focused on emotional and mental issues as I needed to clear out stress, anxiety and worries. But Reiki has helped me on many other levels as well: with insomnia, sciatica (all clear after two years of Reiki), boosting my immune system (from a cold a month to a cold a year) and countless other physical challenges that have cropped up over 17 years of life.

Life still has its ups and downs of course but while chaos may reign outwardly, inwardly all is well with me.

This, I believe, is the key that draws people to Reiki: it gives us the ability to find inner peace, balance and connection. Certainly my own relationship with Reiki has been one of growing serenity and personal awareness and, as we shall see in the following chapters, there are some clear reasons why this happens the way it does. Reiki didn't miraculously and instantly give me the gift of peace, rather it taught me, through regular practice, how to find it for myself. And Reiki can do the same for you; that inner peace exists in all of us.

Chapter 2

The Evolution of Medicine and Reiki

"As medical practitioners
we cannot shut our eyes to
possibilities; to a source of energy
other than calories."

Dr Sudhir Shah, Neurologist

If you were educated in the last century it is likely you grew up, as I did, with an entrenched mechanistic viewpoint, believing life can be explained by the laws of physics and chemistry.

At school, my favourite subject was biology. I loved the details and was fascinated by the miraculous workings of our cellular system. It is easy to see how medical science became so enthralled by it, especially when you take into account the amazing results this field has achieved in the past 100 years in the eradication of many fatal diseases and the technological advances that now allow us to replace almost every body part as it wears out.

This chapter takes a very brief walk through the history of

medicine and serves as a reminder of where we have come from, how our philosophy has been moulded and how, perhaps, it is time for a rethink.

The development of modern medicine

Given all we currently know about the workings of the human body, it's hard to appreciate that 300 years ago renowned thinkers and scientists were in the middle of a great debate about what delineated living from non-living matter. The general belief was that living organisms were 'vital' because they had a spirit or a spark which set them apart from non-living things. In religion that 'vital spark' took the form of God, and in science it took the form of an organizing, non-physical force or element. Medicine, during this era, saw healing as an art – part intuition, part knowledge – in which the patient was very much involved. The healer or doctor provided the catalyst to help the patient find their own 'vital spark', the invigoration of which was a critical element for health and healing.

As science grew increasingly mechanistic, more and more medical doctors and researchers swung towards the idea that life was simply a chemical phenomenon. With wonderful breakthroughs such as the discovery of penicillin in 1929, the advancements in cellular biology and the unravelling of the DNA code, it seemed increasingly conclusive that all human workings could be deciphered via chemical reactions. As a result of this focus on the mechanics of biochemistry, medicine began to treat the body, to put it bluntly, as a robotic machine.

There began a split in thinking between what we know today as conventional medicine and holistic or complementary medicine. Conventional medicine focuses on treating the body when it is already broken or breaking down, and likens the healthy body to a well-oiled machine. Conventional medicine places little emphasis or study as to what keeps us healthy and vital. There is also little research on why some people remain healthy when others around them succumb to viruses and disease, or why some people seem to be able to heal from 'incurable' disease. Advances in conventional medicine are celebrated when researchers discover ways to treat an existing disease or cure an illness that has already taken hold.

In contrast, the focus of holistic medicine is prevention and bolstering the body's own defences to maintain balance. A healthy body is viewed as one in which a strong immunity is developed due to the balance of all body systems – mental, emotional, spiritual, as well as physical. By definition, holistic medicine is vital and maintains a philosophical belief that life is sustained by a 'vital spark'. In Chinese medicine this spark is defined as '*Chi*', in Indian Ayuvedic medicine it is referred to as 'Prana'.

As we enter the 21st Century, the pendulum appears to be swinging back to a more modern form of vitalism. Many of us believe that we are more than the sum of our chemical composition. This may not necessarily mean we believe in a single divine being but, at least for me, it is hard to observe the natural world without believing in some form of spirit or vital spark that continues to pour life into everything around us. In many countries there is a growing backlash against the mechanistic, dehumanising experience of our current medical system and an increasing interest in holistic approaches. Many doctors and medical researchers are themselves leading the shift in thinking to a more balanced approach to health, one that encompasses both the detailed observation of our cellular functions, and the balancing of our vitality, our humanity.

Reiki is gaining greater acceptance in the medical profession and accelerating its reach into hospitals, emergency rooms, operating theatres and care homes. In a 2007 study by the American Hospitals Association, 15% of hospitals in the USA offered Reiki to their inpatients. Andrew Schafer, Chief Physician at New York-Presbyterian Hospital/Weill Cornell Medical Center sums it up by saying "today's complementary and alternative therapies could be tomorrow's medical breakthroughs."[2] In tandem with the growth in popularity of Reiki within medical establishments, Reiki is also one of the fastest growing self-healing therapies.

What is Reiki?

The word 'Reiki' is derived from the Japanese 'Rei' meaning mysterious, divine, spiritual, pure, and 'Ki' meaning vital energy, feelings, life-force. Most Reiki teachers today describe Reiki as being 'Universal Life Energy' but this is possibly quite different from the definition used by Reiki's originator, Mikao Usui, who taught it with a much stronger religious flavour. A flick through existing Reiki literature finds, among many others, the following definitions of Reiki:

> "The Universal Energy of Reiki is a particular frequency that permeates all life" Lawrence Ellyard, *The Tao of Reiki* (p. 119)

> "Primordial consciousness is the source of the healing pulsations we call Reiki." Pamela Miles, *Reiki, A Comprehensive Guide* (p. 189)

> "It [Reiki] is defined as being that power which acts and lives in all created matter" Bodo Gabinski & Shalila Sharamon, *Reiki, Universal Life Energy* (p. 15)

> "Reiki is 'nonpolarised' subatomic energy that is released as a harmonic into energy blueprints that are in a state of disharmony." Dr John & Esther Veltheim, *Reiki, the science, metaphysics and philosophy* (p. 29)

> "Reiki is an energy of an even higher vibration than our normal life-force energy" Penelope Quest, *Self-healing with Reiki* (p. 47)

Reiki, or Universal Life Energy, by my definition, is energy at its purest. It is the life spark or vital energy that is present throughout our universe, the glue that holds all things together. My own belief is that the two separate schools of vitalism and mechanism will become united. As science progresses, so we will continue to see a blurring of lines and the art of medicine will again become more important, as will the patients' part in finding their own healing 'spark'. Hopefully the research and discussion presented in this book will help to pave the way for a more inclusive approach.

How Reiki teaching focus has evolved

The evolution of Reiki is fascinating. Due to the 'flavours' instilled by key individuals along the way, it has become the simple self-help technique it is today and continues to evolve at a rapid pace. Reiki's true history, however, is uncertain and is still being pieced together as more information (and misinformation) comes to light. It is perhaps more of a 'story' than a history, but it does highlight the key players responsible for Reiki's spread outside Japan. (Note that Reiki's evolution in Japan is a very different story.)

The roots of the Reiki tradition that I teach began with a gentleman named Mikao Usui, who was born in 1865 in Japan. According to the inscription on the Usui Memorial located next to his grave in Saihoji Temple[3], Tokyo, he was very learned and did much travelling throughout his early life studying medicine, religion and forms of spiritual development. In March 1922 after a meditation retreat on Mount Kurama he had a powerful spiritual experience (what we consider to have been the first spontaneous attunement to Reiki) and, soon after, realised he had the power to heal others without his own energy being depleted. He subsequently moved to Tokyo and set up a healing society called *Usui Reiki Ryoho Gakkai* (Usui Reiki Healing Society) a society still in existence today. It is believed that Usui trained a total of sixteen teachers (equivalent to Reiki Masters) and thousands of Reiki students before his death in 1926.

Usui was a deeply spiritual man and a practicing Buddhist. His Reiki techniques are mixed with prayer, meditation, and a very intuitive treatment process. According to the research of Frank Arjava Petter[4] and others, Usui used to teach his students in slow stages and only when he felt they were ready could they proceed to the next level. Our current Level One (which is usually taught in 12 hours or less) could take an Usui student months to master.

The second key player in our story is Dr Chujiro Hayashi. Hayashi was a medical doctor trained by Usui in 1925. He had a medical clinic in Tokyo and set up his own *Hayashi Shiki Reiki Ryoho* (Hayashi Reiki Institute). The institute was very popular in its time and seems to have been larger and more successful than the Usui Reiki Healing Society. Hayashi is thought to have trained 17 Reiki Masers before his death in 1940. Hayashi's contribution to Reiki was guided by his medical background. He took an essentially spiritual system and modified the protocols to introduce standardized hand positions for different ailments. In the most part they are obvious first-aid positions (directly over the affected areas) but in some cases the hand positions are designed to help boost major organs and meridians (body energy points) as well.

Hayashi trained Hawayo Takata, the first 'western' Reiki Master, in 1938. Although she was Japanese, Takata was born in Hawaii and came across Hayashi's clinic on a trip back to Japan to visit her parents. She had lung problems and abdominal pains and through treatments at Hayashi's clinic was cured of many of these issues. This motivated Takata to train as a Reiki Master under Hayashi. After her training she established her own clinic in Hawaii and had trained a total of 22 Reiki Masters by the time she died in 1980. It is these Masters who are predominantly responsible for the spread of Reiki in the west.

Takata's contribution resulted from the combination of her Japanese heritage and her western mind. She was allowed access to Reiki because she was Japanese, yet her mind was tuned into the western way of thinking. Her brilliance was in bringing Reiki to America and adapting it to the times. She 'packaged' Reiki so that was accessible to all by simplifying the teachings and making it possible to be trained to Reiki Level One in a weekend.

The fact that Reiki has spread so quickly is testament to this evolution in the time it takes to complete basic Reiki training, and in that respect it is a blessing that these changes took place. The downside of this much faster pace is that many people come to Reiki with a 'quick fix' attitude and often miss the true benefits of the cumulative effects of Reiki over years of patient practice.

In Japan, Reiki is still practised and taught but very little is known about its development. Ironically most of the public Reiki training in Japan is now carried out by western-trained Masters.

There is an enormous variety of blends and techniques using both western and original Japanese teaching.

Elsewhere, Reiki has literally taken the world by storm. In little over forty years since Hawayo Takata first began teaching in Hawaii, Reiki is now found in almost every natural health centre, and millions of people use Reiki in their daily lives.

In summary, ninety years ago, when Usui discovered Reiki, modern medicine and spiritual Reiki seemed poles apart. Medicine believed every human process could be explained mechanistically, via physical cause and effect; a chain of events isolated and linear, like dominoes knocking into one another along a predictable line. In order to 'fix' the body, this chain of events needed to be understood and replicated or manipulated. The assumption was that once the body malfunctioned, it would not be able to fix itself without intervention.

During this same period, Reiki was seen as a spiritual experience that was all encompassing and vital. Reiki was believed to be the life force that flowed through everything and by harnessing this energy and using it in the body we could improve our balance and vitality. Once the body was in balance, it could reset its own processes and fix malfunctions all by itself. The assumption was that although the body could heal itself it was often blocked; the vital spark (or *Chi*) was not moving freely and Reiki could help the body unblock and heal.

Although underlying philosophies have not changed, the paths of Reiki and modern medicine are slowly beginning to converge. Today there is more openness to discover just how much the body is capable of fixing by itself, without medical intervention. In the next chapter we explore why we sometimes experience blocks that prevent us from finding our balance and vitality, and how we can help ourselves to heal.

Chapter 3

Why We Need Healing

"When you are really balanced,
neither leaning on this side
nor leaning on that side, when
you are exactly in the middle,
you transcend."

Osho

Before we go on to look at why we need healing, it is important
to get a working definition for what we mean by 'healing' and to
understand the processes most of us go through that bring us to a
point where healing is necessary.

When I first found Reiki I didn't consider myself sick or in ill
health. I certainly didn't feel that I needed 'curing' in the usual sense
of the word. Apart from sciatica, I was a healthy individual, or so I
thought. But as I continued to explore Reiki and to self-treat over
a period of time, I discovered an entirely different and unexpected
benefit: one defined below as 'the transcendence of suffering'.

In reality I was out of balance, emotionally stressed and unhappy but blaming it all on my external circumstances (if only I could get a pay rise/ find a boyfriend/ get a decent haircut!). I didn't feel 'whole' and I wasn't at peace with myself.

In this chapter we explore healing within the context of wholeness or balance. We explore what happens to our physiology when we are out of balance, and why it is so easy for us to tip into that state.

The definition of healing

In many cultures the word healing has become synonymous with 'curing' which, to my mind, is a very different thing. Curing usually assumes a single minded goal: to rid the body of illness and restore it to health. Healing, on the other hand, is more akin to achieving a 'wholeness' that may or may not include the curing of an illness. Indeed, the very word 'heal' stems from the root *haelan*; the condition or state of being *hal*, or whole. *Hal* is also the root of 'holy,' defined as 'spiritually pure.'[5] To me, feeling 'whole' about your illness, even though you still have it, means you are healed – you are in acceptance and peace.

Although pregnancy is far from being an illness, the experience below is a good illustration of how Reiki can bring acceptance and wholeness without 'cure'.

A pregnant woman came to one of my Reiki courses to help overcome a terrible case of morning sickness. She looked pale and ill throughout the weekend and nibbled anxiously on crackers. It was her first child and she told me the morning sickness was causing her a great deal of worry, especially about how little nutrition her baby was getting. Over the months that followed, I was surprised to learn that the Reiki did not appear to help her symptoms at all. She continued to suffer from morning sickness throughout her nine months of pregnancy but despite her concerns, gave birth to a perfect and healthy baby. When I quizzed her about this she told me that although Reiki had not cured her physical symptoms, it had worked on her anxiety over being sick which was what had been overwhelming her. Reiki had allowed her to accept her symptoms without the trauma. As far as she was concerned the Reiki had worked perfectly.

In 2005, The Annals of Family Medicine[6] conducted a study based on in-depth interviews with leading figures in medicine and holistic health to determine an operational definition of healing. The study found that *"Healing was associated with themes of wholeness, narrative, and spirituality. Healing is an intensely personal, subjective experience involving a reconciliation of the meaning an individual ascribes to distressing events with his or her perception of wholeness as a person."*

Their conclusion was that healing could be operationally defined as ***"the personal experience of the transcendence of suffering."***

This is the definition I will be working with for the purposes of this book; as we heal ourselves with Reiki we experience less suffering and more peace and contentment in our lives because as we heal, we reconnect to our wholeness.

Bringing our system back into balance

There are two avenues to explore when we look at how Reiki heals; first is the physical aspect of our cellular system; second is the role our brain plays in regulating our system and how our thoughts can cause chaos to our ability to find balance. These two avenues often entwine, making it hard to know which one we are travelling along. Exploring both avenues will, however, give us a greater understanding of how Reiki energy works.

How cells use energy

Our cells are constantly active. They are busy making thousands of macromolecules and proteins, transporting substances, contracting muscles, sending electrical messages – and all of these processes require energy. Overlying this activity, the body has an 'operating' system which Bruce Lipton has summarised clearly and simply in his book, *The Biology of Belief.*

Lipton explains that the body's operating system sends instructions out via a single 'on-off' switch. The 'on' position indicates that the body is in growth mode or growth response. The 'off' position indicates protection mode or protection response.

In growth mode our bodies are 'all systems go', using energy to grow and flourish. Billions of cells get replaced every day; our gut lining is replaced every three to five days, our blood cells, skin, and organs are constantly renewing themselves, and in this way our bodies are continually growing. To experience our bodies in full growth mode is to experience vitality.

In the 'off' position, or protection mode, many of the body's vital systems are shut down to conserve energy, this mode is typically referred to as the flight or fight response. In this mode our bodies divert energy away from growth and direct it towards the limbs and brain. Our system closes down and isolates itself from the external environment. To experience our bodies in full protection mode is to experience stress and fear.

The switch cannot be on and off at the same time, we cannot tense *and* relax our muscles at the same time, we cannot be shut off from *and* open to the environment at the same time. In other words, we experience *either* stress *or* vitality – but not both at the same time. It seems that many of us believe that living with stress, or worrying, or trying to meticulously plan and control our lives, will somehow bring us more happiness. Unfortunately, stress simply keeps us switched 'off' and in protection mode; it will never give us the happy outcome we seek – it's biologically impossible. Lipton goes on to observe that, surprisingly, our cells have a natural intelligence about such things: individual cells in a Petri dish will naturally gravitate towards nutrients and away from toxins. In this way our cellular structure is totally aware of its environment and innately knows what is nurturing and what is not.

If our cells (or biological selves) were in charge, our protection response would only be triggered if a true threat to our survival existed. So why is it that in today's society, when we hardly ever face a genuinely life threatening event, we spend so much time in protection response and so experience a great deal more stress and fear than is biologically necessary? For the answer, we need to look at the role our brains play when we start to lose our balance.

The role of our brain

To allow us to function as one co-ordinated organism as opposed to trillions of individual cells our brain overrides the singular cellular activity of our body: it has a bird's eye view and is the operations centre of the body, with an extremely sophisticated monitoring system to judge whether we should be in growth or protection mode.

In a well-balanced human the brain would recognise an external threat and the hypothalamus would send signals to the pituitary (our master gland), which in turn activates the adrenal glands. The adrenals release stress hormones that have many effects on our body. Adrenaline diverts vital energy and blood to our limbs and restricts our digestive and internal organs; this interferes with the generation of energy and the growth processes of the body. Adrenaline prepares our body for immediate action and is accompanied by more rapid heart rate, higher blood pressure and depression of the blood's ability to clot and repair. The Adrenal glands also produce glucocorticoids that depress the immune response. Our immune system requires a lot of energy so restricting it is a logical step if the body is under threat. When our body is in balance we register this threat, respond accordingly and then quickly switch back to growth mode once the threat has passed.

Although we rarely face physical threats to our survival today, our *thinking* still triggers this physiological 'stress' response. Every day when we experience stressful thinking our body goes into protection mode and we shut down our immune system and inhibit our natural cellular growth. Many of us actually spend most of our time in this protection or stress mode and wonder why we are exhausted at the end of the day.

Over the past few decades hundreds of studies have been done on the effect of stress on our immune system. Results have shown that people suffering from chronic stress, or who have a perception that their lives are very stressful, experience a significant reduction in the effectiveness of their immune system[7]. It bears repeating: when we are stressed we go into protection mode which actually causes our immune system to shut down.

It's as if we need to press a reset button to give our body a chance to recalibrate, rest and switch back to growth mode. Over time if we experience more periods of calm, and less periods of stress we will gravitate more frequently towards growth response where we will find greater vitality, stronger immunity and much more peace. This is not some miraculous transformation, but simply the other side of who we naturally are – we have been in protection mode for so long, many of us have forgotten that our growth mode even exists.

Why are we getting so stressed?

It is useful to understand what causes the stress and trauma that switches us to protection mode so easily, and why we struggle to find our way back to the far healthier growth mode.

By going back to our very beginnings we can see how familiar behavioural patterns start to emerge. We arrive out in the big wide world through what many people would say is the single most traumatic event in our lives … our birth.

It's no wonder that babies cry and sleep a lot: they are inundated by stimuli from light, sound, touch and have to piece it all together. What an overwhelming experience at the beginning of life's journey! However, when we arrive amidst all this chaos, we are made ready for it. Our brains are wired to learn effortlessly – we are like eager sponges able to absorb an infinite number of new stimuli, experiences and concepts[8].

Our left brain (the logical part of the brain that also houses our self-consciousness or 'ego') is in charge of making sense of all this new data. To help it catalogue and sift through millions of pieces of information, the logical brain very quickly learns to differentiate between 'good' and 'bad'. In cellular terms we distinguish between 'nutrient' and 'toxin' and in the cave man equivalent, between 'survival' and 'extinction'. Likewise, in modern society we tend to gravitate towards 'reward and pleasure' and move away from 'punishment and pain'. This duality, simplistic as it seems, shapes many of our beliefs, and our actions.

As babies and young children, we quickly learn to differentiate between 'good' and 'bad' categories by paying attention to our environment. We begin to notice that those around us (who we instinctively love and trust) have preferences: they grimace at some of the things we do and laugh and clap at others. The grimace, to our young and receptive brains, feels uncomfortable – almost draining – like a form of punishment. Our brain teaches us to avoid such reactions by behaving in a way that will encourage the laughs and the claps as they make us feel good and more energized.

This pattern of punishment and reward, created through the values and beliefs of our early care givers, becomes hard-wired into our system as we very quickly learn the actions that will bring about one result versus another. This hard-wiring becomes the first of many responses that shift our bodies into protection mode. Any thought or external action that we consider a punishment (ie someone grimaces at us) will set off the stress response that then turns our physiology upside down.

Over time, we build our own complex set of values and judgements – our own philosophy on life – based on these early experiences. Unfortunately this edifice that we have built discon- nects us from our internal world and the real world: the life that we have created around our beliefs seldom seems to live up to our expectations. We respond with feelings of stress; not because life itself has disappointed us, but because our image or belief about life has disappointed us. If we remove the belief, the stress disappears.

"Life is so vast and beliefs are so small; life is so infinite and beliefs are so tiny. Life never fits with any belief, and if you try to

force life into your beliefs you are trying to do the impossible. It has never happened; it cannot happen in the nature of things. Drop all beliefs and start learning how to experience." Osho[9]

We are constantly trying to force life into our framework of beliefs, and this will always be a hopeless endeavour. Every time we fail, every time we are disappointed, we register it as a threat to our survival (more accurately it is a threat to our belief structure but the brain does not differentiate between threat of an ideal and physical threat of survival). As our cells struggle to thrive and our brain continuously thwarts them by switching into protection mode, we can tell that something's 'not quite right'. We normally think the thing that is 'not right' is outside of us and so begins our search for happiness and fulfilment via external stimulation and reward. But the answer is so much simpler than that. The problem is not with our external world, but with our brain. We are literally exhausting ourselves with our thinking.

Taking response-ability

At first glance, it seems an impossible task to prevent our brains from switching to protection mode every time we think a stressful thought, but actually it is easier than it sounds. The first step towards balance is to reclaim our bodies and our minds and to escape the trap of thinking "it's not my fault" and "I can't help it", producing a form of helplessness that heads us straight towards a protection response.

Protection response, and the body's corresponding shut down, is a chemical reaction that is triggered automatically. There is really nothing we can do to stop it once it is triggered. However, it is a "ninety second response"[10] from trigger to release (watch any child to see this in action – one minute screaming the house down, next minute smiling and gurgling like nothing happened).

This means that a minute and a half after the brain registers a perceived threat it is released from protection mode if no actual threat then emerges. For instance, when we think we see something dangerous (like a snake that turns out to be a rope), or we have to jump back from a curb to avoid a car that passes by too close, we feel a surge of adrenaline which subsides quickly and then is gone – this is the normal stress response in action. If we keep the anger or the fear after the threat has passed, we do so out of choice. Indeed, we can keep it going the entire day if we really want to! In the case of the car, for example, we could spend the day mulling over the near miss with thoughts like 'how inconsiderate', 'how reckless', 'how could someone do that?', 'I could have been killed!', 'What would my family have done without me?', 'Life is so dangerous!'. This circular thinking is what creates a prolonged stress response, and *this* is something we can control.

Taking response-ability means first understanding what we are doing to ourselves, and then taking action that helps us to correct and balance our responses (many of which stem from very old beliefs instilled in us from childhood which have become so automatic they are unconscious).

Flicking the switch

Flicking the switch back to growth mode is of utmost importance. To fight even a common cold, we require our immune systems to be working at optimal capacity, but most of us do not take time to nurture ourselves. Rather we continue with our busy schedules and our stressful lives not realising that by trying to power through in our weakened condition, we actually prolong the very thing we are trying to get rid of. Even when we do rest, if our minds are still active with stressful thoughts, the same suppression of our immune system happens. It is not a matter of simply looking after ourselves physically; it is also crucial to take care of our thinking and to learn how to flick the switch when necessary.

If we extend the example to a more devastating illness such as cancer, the stressful thoughts are amplified tenfold as is the physical assault on our body because of the additional burden of the chemotherapy or radiotherapy treatment we will probably go through. So again, our immune system is taking an enormous hit that we need to find ways to counter. In this example both our physical body and our mental processes are affected. The chemotherapy or medication can have debilitating side effects that we need to physically recover from, and our stressful thoughts end up suppressing our immune system delivering a double blow. It's actually a miracle so many of us make it through.

Can you imagine having cancer and actually being calm, peaceful and vital at the same time? What makes it true that life has to be miserable unless everything is perfect ? (And whenever is *that* going to happen?). Why can't we be happy even though we are in debt, or have lost a loved one, or are experiencing disease or challenge in our lives?

Recovering from an illness or steering our way through a particularly tough stage in our lives while we are in growth mode gives us much better odds for successfully getting through it than fighting on in protection mode. Growth mode boosts our immune system as well as our quality of life, yet we have some strange belief in place that to experience happiness *and* illness will in some way engage the illness as a friend and somehow make things even worse. We couldn't be further from the truth. Having disease in our bodies and being happy and vital at the same time does not mean that we are not dealing with it. Happiness and inertia are not the same. In fact when we are happy we experience *more* clarity, *more* decisiveness, *more* action then when we are paralysed by fear.

Flicking the switch back to growth mode allows us to nurture ourselves, and illness is an internal problem that needs that nurture. Essentially the only time we truly need to switch to protection mode is if we literally need to run for our lives, the rest of our time can, and should, be lived out in growth mode.

My friend Cathy is a classic example of 'growth mode' living; she is a deeply-connected, self-aware woman who practices Reiki and has a wonderful gift in many healing therapies. She seriously practices what she preaches. Her father, with whom she had a loving relationship, died recently, and Cathy misses him dearly. However, this is how she describes an experience which, for most people would be seen as an extremely stressful event:

> *The hospital were amazed by the way we handled things, it was all done in such a quick and easy manner. We made decisions as a family and there was no fighting or high emotions, there was no fear. We paid our last respects and turned off the machine. He was gone within minutes. It was such a beautiful experience and we were all there to support each other. One of the nurses told me she had never seen anything like it. Since then I have missed him of course, and it was a very sad few weeks as we adjusted to life without him, but I have to say I feel really fine now. I am giving myself a lot of self-care but I can visit him in my mind whenever I want and I can see so many blessings for us and for him that his passing was so quick and easy. I have learnt that there is no point holding on to grief or sadness, it doesn't help anyone. I remember him joyfully and with gratitude.*

In the following chapters we look at how each of us can regain our balance, our wholeness, by flicking the switch back to growth mode. We do this by providing our bodies with a limitless supply of energy and then our bodies do the rest. Our bodies are magnificent machines and given the right conditions we flourish effortlessly. With a limitless supply of energy we can promote the repair and healthy functioning of our cellular system on the one level, and help our overworked brain to calm and reset on another. These two distinct pathways are explored in more detail as we look now at how Reiki operates.

Chapter 4

How Reiki Operates

"My life has become significantly more balanced. I am allowing myself to be guided into decisions instead of agonizing over them. Life has become an enjoyable journey for me. I cannot imagine one single day without Reiki!"

Michele, Reiki Practitioner

Reiki energy, or Universal Life Energy, brings us back into balance. Reiki achieves this by operating along two different pathways. The first pathway (the 'energy pump') affects our physiology directly, while the second pathway (the 'peace' pathway) helps calm our overworked brains. Both pathways operate simultaneously and will result in different benefits for different people, depending on their individual priorities. For example, if I am suffering from a physical illness then the energy pump pathway will attract the most Reiki, whereas if I am suffering from stress, Reiki energy will operate along the peace pathway.

This amazing energy source we are tapping into has no inherent qualities of its own; it is neutral energy at its purest. Like potential energy (for example, energy present in calories that is dormant until released by our cells), it is inert until 'funnelled' into the body via our hands. Reiki energy will drive whatever work needs to be done: on a physiological level it can be used to repair damaged cells, reproduce, build immunity, create more efficient communication between different parts of the body, or release toxins. On a mental or emotional level it can be used to promote relaxation and calm.

Reiki as an energy pump

Reiki's first pathway is illustrated most dramatically in physiological improvements such as a faster mending of broken bones or recovery from illness, as well as a stronger immune response. This pathway is likened to a simple energy pump fuelling our body so that our cellular life can flourish.

In osmotic terms there is a flow from high Universal Life Energy (the air surrounding us) to low Universal Life Energy (our tired and exhausted bodies!). The energy will flow as long as there is a difference in concentration. When there is no longer a difference in concentration, the body is in equilibrium. When Reiki is flowing along this pathway it is drawn to areas of high need, it is an automatic process that requires no conscious direction or focus on our part.

The results of this energy pump can be very dramatic. In The Reiki Centre Survey we received hundreds of reports detailing significant improvements in physical well-being.

"I had been struggling with IBS (Irritable Bowel Syndrome) for most of my life. I missed many days of school and cost my parents lots in doctor bills, just to be told it was all in my head and dismiss it with some anti-anxiety medication. One horribly bad day I was huddled over in pain, crying in my room, my mother had recently received her Level One Reiki attunement and offered to just see if it

would help me at all. I was very sceptical and wanted to brush off the idea, but being in that much pain I was willing to try anything. I was not really open to the idea of Reiki and probably never would have studied it had it not been for what happened next. Within a few minutes of treatment, the muscles in my stomach started to relax, the pain receded, and the warmth of the energy flow was amazing. After ten minutes, the pain was almost non-existent. I was so amazed I had to learn more about how this was possible and how I could do this myself... After my attunement I was able to treat my own IBS symptoms and in recent years have basically overcome the condition completely." Asa

"I was diagnosed with Fibromyalgia a decade ago and, as the symptoms progressed, my world became smaller and smaller, to the point where I rarely left the house and was unable to do many of the activities I enjoyed. I always experienced relief from Reiki, and once I began doing self-Reiki daily, the effects lasted longer. These days, I'm walking and playing with the dog, shovelling snow, starting up my holistic therapies business and generally doing what I want when I want." Victoria

"I have multiple sclerosis and without Reiki I believe that I would not be walking today. For almost nine months I wasn't able to walk, but after starting Reiki (my partner and I do Reiki almost daily on one another) I was walking again within three months and off crutches and cane completely after six more! The pain is greatly decreased as well as the muscle spasms." Anonymous

"My spastic colon pain was impeding my ability to do college work so my doctor put me on Phenergan, a tranquillizer. It stopped the pain but made me sleepy all the time, which was almost as bad. I had one Reiki treatment, during which the practitioner's hands got incredibly hot – so hot my skin was left with red handprints for a few minutes afterwards. The spastic colon condition disappeared immediately: I never had another symptom and never had to take

another pill for it. I also used to have sinus infections, more or less on a monthly basis, as a result of severe allergies to pollen, dust, mould, mites, grasses, trees, cats, etc. That meant taking almost constant antibiotics, which had a terrible effect on my gastrointestinal system's helpful bacteria. Since treating myself regularly with Reiki, I very rarely get a sinus infection – maybe once a year – and that's usually when I get too busy to keep up with my self-treatment routine." Leslie

As well as being responsible for the dramatic physical improvements cited above, it is the flow of energy from Universal Life Energy into usable energy for the body that creates many of the physical sensations reported by Reiki practitioners such as heat, tingling and vibration.

According to The Reiki Centre Survey of 546 Reiki practitioners, the vast majority of respondents experience Reiki as a sensation. Only 4% do not. Of the 96% who do experience sensations, by far the most prevalent are heat, tingling and cold. Others include vibrations, pressure, pulsing, electric shocks, pulling/magnetic sensations, popping, light or colours, heaviness or sleepiness. [11]

However, everyone experiences Reiki differently. It is not a physical energy force (such as heat or light) that we are used to experiencing with one of our five senses and, although practitioners describe a lot of sensations, it is notable that they are *different* sensations. If Reiki was a physical energy such as heat, everyone would experience it the same way. Often when Reiki flows through the hands and into the body, the mind struggles to categorize the experience (if indeed it is aware of experiencing anything at all). Many novices may not experience any sensations until they have practiced Reiki for some time and become more accustomed to feeling for the energy present.

Stimulating the brain's peace centres

The second pathway tackles our overworked minds by using Reiki energy for calming. Here, Reiki works much like meditation and our brain uses it to promote alpha and theta brain waves.

The brain is seen to produce different frequencies of electrical activity across its neurons depending on what it is doing. Alpha waves are predominantly associated with states of relaxation, a calm wakefulness. These waves can be produced by closing your eyes, relaxing and becoming still. Theta waves are more predominant in skilled meditators and represent a quiet watchfulness – the mind watching its thoughts. Both types of waves denote relaxation and a stopping of active, busy or anxious thinking, or active concentration, which produces beta waves.

> *"Alpha wave type has been used as a universal sign of relaxation during meditation and other types of rest. The amount of alpha waves increases when the brain relaxes from intentional, goal-oriented tasks. This is a sign of deep relaxation, but it does not mean that the mind is void. Spontaneous wandering of the mind is something you become more aware of and familiar with when you meditate. This default activity of the brain is often underestimated. It probably represents a kind of mental processing that connects various experiences and emotional residues, puts them into perspective and lays them to rest."* Professor Øyvind Ellingsen, Norwegian University of Science and Technology (NTNU)[12]

The promotion of alpha waves into the body system has a dramatic effect on our stress levels by resetting us back to growth mode. In my opinion, using Reiki in this way is its most powerful benefit as it brings us growth, peace and vitality.

Reiki, like meditation, affects the brain by loosening its grip and helping us to release more and more energy and resources to the rest of the body. The active brain consumes more than 20% of the total energy required by the body (but only weighs about 2% of total bodyweight)[13]. Although there has not been extensive research on the amount of energy consumed by the brain in beta state versus alpha or theta, if you carry out your own simple experiment of relaxing quietly versus actively trying to problem solve, it is fairly clear which activity is more exhausting.

Meditation, for years, has been known in the East to be extremely health giving, calming and beneficial. Most Reiki practitioners attest to the similarities between Reiki and meditation, especially when it comes to the results they feel. When we asked respondents in The Reiki Centre Survey to report on the most significant change or improvement they have noticed since starting Reiki, we received many answers similar to those below:

> *"An overall calmness and balance."* Li

> *"I feel more content, self-confident, peaceful."* Anonymous

> *"A sense of the body at a deeper level. A feeling that the body can be treated energetically. Empowerment."* Charlie

> *"I feel so much more at peace now. I feel I have better direction in life. Just thinking about Reiki causes the energy to flow through my body and it makes me feel so happy. I have noticed that I have a much calmer outlook on life; I worry less and I look at things from such a positive angle now. I feel I am here to be happy and by being so help others to be happy."* Suzanne

As the art of meditation spreads to the West, research is confirming its qualities. Dr Andrew Newberg[14] has run several experiments on expert meditators to find that there is a difference in the way their brain's function compared with non-meditators. Specifically, there was a decrease in activity in the left brain, resulting in less brain chatter. Over time, when meditators are not meditating they show increased alertness, consciousness and empathy with others. In Dr Newberg's recent research involving non-meditators who were given a chant to practice for eight weeks, results similar to those among the expert meditators were shown.[15] Specifically:

- ➤ An improvement in memory function as well as other brain functions that tend to deteriorate with age, such as co-ordination, and cognition.
- ➤ Increased focus, clarity and attention span.
- ➤ Lowering of anxiety, irritability, as well as enhanced social awareness.

These results show that anyone can learn to lessen the hold of their busy brains in a very short period of time and with little effort. The Reiki Centre Survey found that respondents noticed improvements very similar to those mentioned above. Nearly 70% of respondents reported a reduction in their levels of anxiety, worry and stress in less than one year. Correspondingly, over the same period, over 70% of respondents noticed an increase in their levels of self-love, peace and contentment, with this figure rising to over 85% of respondents over a longer period of time.[16]

Since the Survey only captured data in yearly blocks, the improvements could have been noticed within weeks or months, certainly the qualitative responses indicate respondents saw changes soon after beginning self-Reiki, and this would mirror my own experience and the experience of many of my students. Reiki seems to follow very similar pathways to meditation by lighting up the intuitive (right) side of our brain that resonates with connection, empathy, oneness and wholeness therefore increasing our feelings of contentment, peace and happiness. In other words, it resets our brains and allows us to experience life in growth mode, or our natural state of being.

Within us, we all have equal capacity to be happy or sad; stressed or peaceful; logical or intuitive; it all depends on our focus and, as we see below, the results can be startling.

Jill Bolte Taylor, in her book *My Stroke of Insight*, tells her incredible story of recovery after a massive stroke that left her logical left brain severely compromised. In her eight-year recovery she learned, through personal experience, the way her brain could rewire and relearn to a point where she believes she is now fully recovered. Her account is fascinating on many levels (not least because she herself is a neuroanatomist) as it highlights the extreme functions of the left and right sides of the brain. When she lost the use of her left brain hemisphere due to a massive haemorrhage (which shut down the majority of her logical functions) she was left with only the functions of her right brain:

> *"From a neuroanatomical perspective, I gained access to the experience of deep inner peace in the consciousness of my right mind when the language and orientation association areas in the left hemisphere of my brain became non functional."* Jill Bolte Taylor, *My Stroke of Insight*, p. 142

How I interpret her experience is that her logical mind could no longer trigger her stress response, she could no longer formulate thinking that caused her adrenal glands to over-activate and, as a result, she experienced life in growth mode. In her story she describes deep peace and connectedness as if she gained a direct experience of what her cellular life felt like without the constant vigilance of her logical mind.

> *"My stroke of insight is that at the core of my right hemisphere consciousness is a character that is directly connected to my feeling of deep inner peace. It is completely committed to the expression of peace, love, joy, and compassion in the world."* Jill Bolte Taylor, *My Stroke of Insight*, p. 140

Thankfully, Reiki can provide an access point which allows us to experience inner peace without having to suffer the trauma of a brain haemorrhage by encouraging the meditative effects as described by Dr Newberg and others. The key difference between Reiki and meditation is the technique used to gain the same result: with Reiki the simple application of your hands on your body is enough to begin the energy flow, and as long as you are willing to stay still and quiet for long enough, you will experience the same effects of meditation without the discipline required to clear the mind or focus. Certainly, for me, this has been an important benefit, as I doubt I would have come this far if Reiki had been a painstakingly difficult and disciplined journey.

Reiki produces a sense of well-being and peace in our lives. This aspect of Reiki opens the door for many Reiki practitioners to look deeper into their lives and priorities. It is not uncommon for people who regularly self-Reiki to undergo radical shifts in their way of thinking, in their life purpose and reported feelings of clarity, focus and personal mission.

"I proceed through life in an entirely different way now, taking care to nourish my body, mind, heart and soul. I've always taken great care of others yet now I've learned to care for myself! Becoming more aware and discerning of my actions, I take responsibility to change those things that are incongruent with my beliefs or hindering my personal growth. Everything seems much more intense now but the profound strength of emotions or situations being experienced are recognized as gifts of opportunity, provoking and enabling me to make necessary changes." Rosie

As Reiki works in our minds and bodies to promote a more balanced energy system, it frees us up to reconnect with ourselves and our lives. It is this awakening to our true selves that is one of the major joys of Reiki.

Chapter 5
Using Reiki for Healing

"I have finally found the key. The love within myself and my own heart."

Nina, Reiki Practitioner

Everyone awakens differently. In The Reiki Centre Survey, although the majority of respondents experience improvements and benefits after practising Reiki, there is a minority who do not. Why is that?

Every individual is unique and so is every individual's journey with Reiki. **It's important to remember that Reiki itself is not 'doing' anything**; it is simply providing the fuel – the energy – for you to do your own inner work. When I give my courses and introduce Reiki to others I often tell of my own big 'wow' moment when I went from insomniac to sleeping beauty after starting Reiki. This change was of such enormous and lasting benefit to me that it has remained my own personal testament to what self-Reiki can achieve. Despite repeatedly telling people that Reiki is unique for each person and everyone responds differently to it, I continue to get occasional irate phone calls from insomniacs complaining they are still not sleeping well after two weeks of self-Reiki. Interestingly though, they do often report improvements in other areas. As discussed in chapter four, Reiki energy follows our body's priorities, not our ego's priorities and its effects can often be unexpected. The Iceberg Concept helps to explain what is really going on.

The Iceberg Concept

Healing is commonly defined as the disappearance of symptoms and a return to feeling 'normal' (until the next time!). In this book, healing is defined as 'the transcendence of suffering', which is not the same as returning to 'normal'. Healing is often much deeper than a simple elimination of symptoms.

The difference that this approach to healing can make is explained here: If I have frequent headaches I could take painkillers to relieve the symptoms, but I might then find myself in a constant cycle of medication and with no permanent alleviation of my suffering. If, however, I acknowledge my headache as being a symptom of a deeper disharmony, I can begin to investigate, within myself, what its cause may be.

Imagine that the illness or problem we are trying to heal is an iceberg, with 70-90% of it hidden from view. What we see above the surface is actually the symptom, in this case, the headache. When we discuss the Iceberg Concept during my courses we come up with dozens of potential reasons for the headache: environmental reasons (light, heat, noise, pollution, etc); allergies; biochemical imbalances; emotional issues such as stress or anxiety; tiredness; back problems; tumours or lumps; concussion; the list is endless! I might have a headache because of one or two of these factors, or maybe because of all of them. But it is logical that the content of my iceberg will be different to yours, and that my healing journey will also be different in both route and length. Every body is different and so is every body's healing journey.

Reiki defies clinical trial (as it is defined today) because it heals the cause – the whole iceberg – not just the symptom, or tip of the iceberg. Whereas medical science may be able to examine a migraine sufferer and deduce which drug should be prescribed to block or suppress a particular neurotransmitter that is relaying the pain to the brain, Reiki will not work in this way. Reiki energy will be used by the body based on its cellular priorities (often working on the underlying cause of the migraine) – and this is likely to be very different from one migraine sufferer to another.

If 50 migraine sufferers each had five Reiki treatments the responses would be so varied and would show improvement at such different rates, that the overall result would be inconclusive. In the case of a migraine caused, for example, by a simple chemical imbalance, Reiki can help the body to rebalance and recovery could be quick and complete. No more migraines! However, if the cause of the migraine is rage, stress, suppressed emotions, or a combination of several long-standing and less straightforward issues, it is equally possible that the migraine will get worse after a Reiki treatment, and it is very likely that it will take a lot longer for the Reiki energy to do its job.

As an illustration, here is a case study of two clients who both suffered from migraines, but whose 'icebergs' were caused by very different issues, and who responded to Reiki in two very different ways:

Client A, a woman in her 40s, came to me for treatments as she was suffering from migraines that left her lying in a darkened room for at least 48 hours. She had tried all types of medication, as well as Chinese herbs and acupuncture, without success. She came to Reiki as a last ditch attempt, on the recommendation of a friend. During our first session together she experienced a deep release of emotion and cried heavily for about 30 minutes. Afterwards, she described going back to the memory of when she was a young child and witnessing her parents go through a violent and aggressive divorce. All her frustration, fear and confusion was released during that one session. She reported feeling lighter and, quite frankly, amazed that she had blocked such powerful emotions within herself for so long. We arranged for two follow-up sessions, which passed without incident, and I know she did not experience any further migraines for at least the next four years (after which time I lost touch with her).

Client B, a man also in his 40s, came to me for treatment at the request of his girlfriend who hoped that Reiki would help him overcome his depression. As we spoke it became clear that he was suffering from a wide variety of problems including depression, immune system weaknesses and a general malaise that his life was not 'turning out the way he wanted'. The first treatment passed without incident but he called me 24 hours later complaining of a terrible migraine. He had not mentioned the migraines during our session but now, on the phone, he reported having them infrequently – but not usually as bad as this. We continued with another two treatments but the migraines continued unabated. Miraculously (to my eyes), during our final session he admitted to me that the Reiki had helped him realize he had a lot of 'sorting out' to do and that the migraines were his internal alarm system, telling him he needed to get his life back on track. I was surprised that after three sessions his mind had opened so quickly to this possibility. I did not see him again after that but I can presume the Reiki sessions did not help his migraines, but gave him something possibly more valuable: a wake-up call.

Both these clients had very different iceberg profiles for the same symptom. Client A's iceberg was connected to pent up emotions that were causing a blockage in her energy system resulting in headaches. Once the emotions around her childhood memory released, so did the problem. Client B's iceberg contained many different issues and, by my estimation, was a much larger iceberg. It stands to reason that he would require more Reiki to see a result as the 'melting' would be a much longer process.

Optimising Reiki

Research done by The Reiki Centre gives us a direct insight into how we can access the most benefit from Reiki. The data points to a strong correlation between both amount of hours of Reiki practiced each week and the number of years practiced. That is to say, Reiki benefits are cumulative and respondents who are using Reiki regularly achieve the best results. Overall, those respondents doing less than one hour of self-Reiki a week have a 50/50 chance of noticing any improvements. These results shift noticeably when the respondent is doing one or more hours a week, in other words there is a weekly routine or commitment in place. Those respondents using self-Reiki as a daily practice see the greatest results; on average they are three times more likely to report benefits.[17]

An apple a day

As Reiki energy is used by our bodies, we may notice an improvement in function and wellness but it does not mean we will remain healthy. If we maintain a self-destructive lifestyle, Reiki may help to relieve certain symptoms temporarily, but it is unlikely any permanent change will occur. Essentially, Reiki is a tool and an aid but it will not take the junk food out of our mouths and forbid us to eat it! Reiki is like the fuel we put into our car, we need to fill up the car regularly for it to run (regular self-Reiki treatments), but how we take care of our car depends solely on the way we drive and maintain it. No amount of fuel will save a car from neglect.

From a physical, cellular viewpoint, energy is used up as quickly as it goes in (much as we need to keep eating in order to fuel our body and replenish lost minerals and vitamins). If we go to a Reiki practitioner for a Reiki treatment and then stop going, or if we self-Reiki for a time and then stop, Reiki energy will be used up, and it will not be long before balance flicks back into imbalance – or growth mode flicks back to protection mode.

"I have been wrestling with depression for years. When I received Reiki sessions from other practitioners I did get a little better, but it didn't last long. After I was attuned and began self-treatments it made all the difference in the world. This is not

something that should be delegated to someone else; our well-being is our own responsibility. Self-Reiki becomes an extremely enjoyable routine that brings untold benefits." Julie

The Reiki Centre Survey provides stark comparisons showing what a difference an hour's Reiki a day can make:

Percentage of respondents reporting improvements in specific symptoms based on number of hours of self-Reiki.		
Symptom	Respondents doing less than 1 hour a week self-Reiki	Respondents doing 7 hours or more a week self-Reiki
Muscle pain/cramp	38%	68%
Back pain/problems	43%	73%
Headaches/ migraines	52%	76%
Colds/flu	58%	80%

Self-Reiki gives you the tool to keep yourself full of energy and allows you to regulate how much you need, and how often. A regular preventative self-Reiki treatment will keep you in balance, improve your immune system and begin the journey of healing.

Transcending suffering

As well as keeping our body in balance and full of energy (the energy pump pathway), Reiki also plays a part in keeping us connected to ourselves via its positive effects on our brain's peace centres. Of those practicing self-Reiki daily, 88% experienced a reduction in stress, 92% an increase in peace and contentment, and 93% experienced greater happiness.[18]

When following the peace pathway – calming our minds and promoting alpha and theta brain waves – Reiki energy helps us to reconnect with ourselves and as a result helps us to become more aware of – and break – our self-destructive patterns. The more balanced we are the more clearly we can see our own needs and the better choices we make. Although this sounds like self-help 101, many of our self-destructive habits are hidden from us in shrouds of denial and circular thoughts. If you are a smoker or a binge eater/drinker you may be well aware of your habit and yet cannot understand why you still struggle. How can Reiki help in this situation? In my own experience, Reiki will help by restoring balance. When you are calm, at peace and connected to yourself, do you need the cigarette/chocolate cake/drink to pep you up or mask your pain?

"I am in better shape to take care of myself, I am a better guide for myself. I handle tough times and situations much better, I don't feel like a victim, I have control of my life" Annette

"Reiki has been wonderful in helping me with issues of self-worth and self-acceptance." Anonymous

"I am able to let go of issues or worries much more quickly." Anonymous

"Reiki has allowed me to access a deep level inside myself that carried a paralysing fear from an early childhood experience. I have been able to face the fear, release it and walk forward with a new strength and confidence." Anonymous

These Reiki practitioners have found deeper awareness through Reiki, but they have also followed through with committed and enthusiastic change. The people who notice changes are the ones who make them happen. Reiki is a wonderful support mechanism but our own awareness of what we are doing, and subsequent action, is what is paramount in ringing the changes necessary for transcendence of suffering.

Very recently I had a conversation with a student of mine who was desperately trying to help her mother battle cancer. She felt that whenever she dedicated a stretch of time to giving her mother Reiki, her mother improved. But as soon as she focussed her attention back to her own life, her mother regressed. She felt she was going one step forward, two steps back, and she was understandably frustrated. It is the hardest thing to tell someone they cannot 'cure' a loved one, but this is the truth. All the Reiki energy in the universe cannot miraculously 'cure' someone. If Reiki is the fuel, the driver is still in control of the vehicle and still gets to decide the direction of the journey. If you are trying to change something in yourself but you are not willing to do something different, you have a slim chance of seeing that change manifest. In the case of another person, it is even more hopeless to try to change them! All you can do is provide the fuel and hope it gives them the energy needed to shift. No matter how much Reiki the mother receives, if she continues to live in protection mode or continues to harbour negative or destructive thoughts, her cellular structure will continue its self-destructive spiral as there is no opportunity for the cells to truly flourish.

> *"I can tell you that if you choose to see a world full of love, your body will respond by growing in health. If you choose to believe that you live in a dark world full of fear, your body's health will be compromised as you physiologically close yourself down in a protection response."* Bruce Lipton, PhD, *The Biology of Belief*, p. 113

In Bruce Lipton's book *The Biology of Belief* he explains that our DNA and genes do not control our cells, rather our DNA responds to signals from outside our cells, including the energy messages of our thoughts. This is a very powerful idea and one that is growing in support as other scientists are also finding that genetics is only one piece of a much more complex puzzle. As we have seen, our thoughts control our protection/growth response and we have a high level of choice in whether or not we choose to keep the protection response running with negative or circular thinking. There are also many examples of 'beating the odds' when it comes to illness and disease, suggesting that we can also have an incredibly positive impact on our bodies' healing power.

In a wonderfully dramatic example, Lipton relates the story of Pettenkofer, a critic of Robert Koch's Germ Theory, who famously demonstrated the strength of his belief (or lack of belief) in 1892 by drinking a quantity of water infected by pure cultures of the cholera bacillus. To everyone's astonishment, Pettenkofer did not develop cholera. Somehow his strong belief that the water was harmless protected him from the deadly disease[19]. It bears emphasizing this point: his strong belief protected him from a deadly disease!

Medical literature is littered with similar examples of patients who beat the odds and experience 'miraculous' recovery, the medical term for it is spontaneous remission and, surprisingly, very little research is actually done on this group of people. This anomaly, however, suggests that we are not at the mercy of disease, pathogens and circumstance unless we abdicate responsibility for ourselves to others.

Does that mean we never get ill, or that we live forever? Of course not, everyone goes through the same cycle of birth, growth, decay and death – none of us can escape this! It is how we respond to this cycle that ensures us a happy or unhappy life.

If we focus on radiating gratitude and love we are giving off very different thoughts and empowering our cellular structure in a very different way (by being in growth mode) than if we are radiating anger or despair (protection mode). A growing body of scientific evidence points to the inescapable conclusion that we are masters of our own health. Studies on the level of optimism linked to stroke incidence (the higher the level of optimism, the less likely to have a stroke)[20]; experiments on stress and anger related to hypertension (the more angry/stressed you are the more likely to develop the disease)[21]; and the powerful effect of hope and faith on post operation recovery time[22] point to just some of the areas that we can affect with our minds.

Usui's Five Principles

Usui was well aware of the mind's powerful influence on our well-being. He taught five Reiki life principles to be contemplated, 'just for today':

1. I will not anger
2. I will not fear
3. I will live the attitude of gratitude

4. I will do my work honestly
5. I will show love and respect for every living thing

> *"The ultimate goal is to understand the ancient secret method for gaining happiness and thereby discover an all-purpose cure for many ailments."* From Usui's Memorial.[23]

Usui asked his students to meditate on these principles every morning and evening and believed that this contemplation would bring greater self-awareness. He also knew that Reiki alone would not be sufficient to create lasting healing; a radical shift in thinking and action had to follow as well.

So how to live these principles in real life? I have noticed, thankfully, that the principles grow easier to follow with more self-Reiki. I also place great emphasis on the precursor 'just for today' and remind myself that if I fail, tomorrow is another 'just for today' to strive for. 'Just for today' means to be more present. When you are totally present the world is a very nurturing place, everything you need for that moment is right in front of you; the air you breath, the floor that supports you. When you are really present, the five principles live through you naturally.

The first two principles remind us not to be in protection mode unnecessarily. The third principle reminds us to be in growth mode as much as possible. The final two principles are guides for our actions; being true to ourselves by doing our life's work (which is not the same as our career) honestly; and showing kindness and respect for others. If all our actions are guided by these two principles then we will truly understand the meaning of healing.

Usui's principles are the guiding light for most Reiki Masters and, hopefully, for most practitioners of Reiki; they are seen as an important part of our healing process. Simply using self-Reiki with no contemplation will of course give you temporary results and increased vitality and energy. But combining the benefits of self-Reiki with a more grateful and reverent outlook on life is an extremely powerful (and I would say critical) combination for the transcendence of suffering.

We are ultimately responsible for our own state of energy, and for creating the best possible environment for our cellular structure to flourish. Reiki energy can help to 'fill us up' and may 'unblock' energy in our system that may lead to spontaneous remission, but this is the exception rather than the rule. Most often, self-Reiki gives us a feeling of peace and calm to help us see more clearly the areas of our life that need changing, but then it is up to us to actually make the changes.

"I've practiced Reiki for 35 years now, so physical conditions have come and gone and new ones have arisen. Most often Reiki has eased or eliminated these problems. The first area that transcends aging is my awareness, desire and capacity to practice and live the Usui Five Principles. Another is the daily sense of well-being and connection that comes with self-treatment." Susan

Chapter 6

Becoming a Reiki Practitioner

"I cannot even imagine how people manage without Reiki. My life has purpose and joy and everyday is a blessing, all of this I attribute to Reiki."

Lynn, Reiki Practitioner

So why choose Reiki?

I have come to respect all forms of healing therapy and believe that each one has an important part to play in keeping us healthy and happy. Many therapies (both holistic and conventional) provide excellent results and support and my belief is that each of us will be drawn to different systems depending on what we need at any given time.

However, to my knowledge and within my own experience, there are no other therapies that can boast such an all-encompassing reach or offer such a breadth of benefits as Reiki. It is the innate qualities of Reiki – its very essence – that make it so unique.

Before we move on to the practicalities of Reiki training, it is worth considering the unique qualities of Reiki in more detail, and how these qualities could impact on your own experience with Reiki.

Qualities of Reiki

We have already touched upon two of Reiki's unique qualities in previous chapters:

1. **Reiki energy is osmotic**: Reiki energy flows as if by osmosis and once it enters the body it will be used where it is most needed. There is no requirement to direct the energy. No extensive training is necessary to achieve excellent results.
2. **Reiki energy is all-encompassing**: It works on all levels: physical, mental and emotional. 'One size fits all' due to the neutral or inert state of the energy as it enters the body. The energy is *used by* the body and does not *act on* the body.

Three further qualities that help make Reiki such a foundational healing therapy are discussed more fully below:

3. **Reiki energy flows automatically**: Using our hands as energy funnels, Reiki will 'switch' itself on or off with no personal effort, no skill, or special gift required by us. Anyone can be attuned to Reiki.
4. **Reiki energy is complementary:** Due to its inert quality, Reiki is complementary with any other form of healing or medication. There are no known contra-indications.
5. **Reiki energy is universal and limitless:** Reiki does not use up personal energy or drain you in any way. Neither does it rely on your state of health. People who are already very sick can use Reiki to treat themselves or others.

Reiki is automatic

Reiki energy switches itself on and off without any conscious effort or belief on the practitioner's part. This quality manifests itself whether Reiki is being *given* or *received*. The hands are used as instruments to facilitate the flow of Reiki energy and they act as funnels or channels. In normal daily life, Reiki practitioners' hands are at rest, they are not funnelling Reiki energy as the environment is in equilibrium.

For example, while I am typing this, my hands are touching either the air or the inanimate computer keyboard and, as there is no difference in the energy needs of either the air or the keyboard, my hands do not channel energy and are at rest. If I stop and place my hands on my stomach, I will notice that they 'activate' as the Reiki energy is naturally drawn into them and funnelled into my body. In my experience, my abdomen, shoulders, and lower back are my 'hot spots' and are always in need of an energy boost! Once I move my hands back to the keyboard they 'switch off' once again. This may sound like a strange phenomenon, but actually it is quite reassuring, and over the years it has become so natural that it rarely registers unless I turn my attention towards my hands to see what is actually going on down there!

To check my theories I like to experiment, and over the years my husband has proved to be an excellent guinea pig. Although he himself has been attuned to Reiki, he does not use it much in his daily life, so for the most part is not conscious of it and does not feel much sensation in his hands. However, if I place his hand on my back or stomach when he is asleep, I can feel the Reiki flowing as strongly as if he was actively giving me a treatment. The Reiki energy flows regardless of the fact he is not conscious of my (or his) actions. That he does not really believe he is qualified to give Reiki to anyone else substantiates the theory that Reiki is not a system based on belief, since his hands so obviously funnel Reiki whenever he touches me, whether he believes it or not. This lack of conscious effort is also clearly demonstrated when attuning animals and young children to Reiki, as the following story illustrates.

Many years ago I visited the elderly aunt of a friend of mine. The aunt was suffering from arthritis and was wheelchair bound. She had a lot of pain in her knees which I hoped Reiki could alleviate.

While I was giving her Reiki I noticed her cat spent most of its time sitting on her lap with its paws hanging over her knees. I gave the cat an attunement to see if it would make a difference. My thinking was that every time the cat sat in the aunt's lap, she would give her owner Reiki and help with her pain. Wonderfully, my hunch paid off. The aunt experienced much less pain and said she could feel the warmth pouring out of her cat's paws.

Reiki is complementary

When treating yourself or others with Reiki, there is no need to make a diagnosis or be concerned about other treatments which might be taking place concurrently. This is because Reiki is a neutral energy, inert until it is funnelled into the body. In other words it has no predictable quality or frequency so it is both complementary to other forms of treatment – such as chemotherapy – and safe to use when other treatments might be precluded – such as for pregnant women and babies. The fact that there are no contra-indications with Reiki is an important benefit.

By comparison, conventional medication and many other holistic therapies require diagnosis and prognosis. The doctor or therapist needs to take a detailed medical history in order to make their diagnosis because the medication or course of treatment that is prescribed will have a predictable and directed effect on the body. In the case of conventional medicine, a predominantly chemical reaction will have specific effects on certain parts of the body. In the case of holistic treatments such as acupuncture, aromatherapy, Chinese herbs, and many other energy therapies, there is a specific movement of energy that is triggered by the treatment, and that movement can have conflicting effects on other treatments being prescribed at the same time. St John's Wort (a herbal remedy for depression), for example, is known to counteract the effect of Warfarin (a medication to prevent blood clotting). Some pressure and acupuncture points should not be used on pre-existing conditions such as heart disease. And massage should not be used in conjunction with a long list of conditions including inflammation, fever, high blood pressure, cancer and diabetes. This is why it is important to tell your physician if you are in the care of other therapists who are also prescribing treatments. It is recommended that you tell your physician if you are having Reiki treatments, but only so that he or she can monitor improvements that might not otherwise be expected.

The following personal story illustrates how Reiki can help not only to diminish the effects of chemotherapy treatment but also to heal in the deepest of ways:

Over ten years ago I had the privilege of teaching Reiki to a family who used it to help their mother overcome much discomfort. She had been diagnosed with level four breast cancer and had been given six months to live. When the family first came to me it was with the hope that Reiki would ease the stress and fear of death. They all wanted to experience their mother's passing as a peaceful event; I was very humbled by their openness and courage.

Over the next six months the most extraordinary thing happened: not only did the mother continue to improve, but she outlived all her doctors' expectations and two years after the prognosis she was declared cancer-free. She credited Reiki for significantly diminishing the side effects of her chemotherapy; notably, keeping her appetite, suffering much less nausea and enjoying greater levels of vitality during the treatment process. When she had her breasts removed she also told me the wounds seemed to heal very quickly leaving her with much less scarring than she had expected. She had a wonderful sense of humour, declaring that Reiki also helped her hair grow back quicker!

I learnt a great deal from this remarkable woman; it was my first experience working with someone so deeply and intimately. It also taught me that Reiki is a tool, not some miracle cure. Eventually she did succumb to cancer and at the time I was devastated. I had expected the Reiki to 'save' her and felt somehow betrayed. I had fallen into the common trap of believing that Reiki itself was the 'cure' and forgetting that, while Universal Life Energy provides fuel, healing and cure are not the same thing. Over time I have come to see that Reiki's gift to this wonderful woman was for her to be able to enjoy three unanticipated years of fulfilling life with her loving family. Reiki had truly helped this woman to transcend her suffering.

Reiki is universal and limitless

Because Reiki energy is drawn from a universal source, when one person gives Reiki to another (or to themselves), they are not depleting their own energy source. This means that even very sick people, with very little energy of their own, can still give Reiki to themselves or others very effectively.

This next story is a lovely example of the benefits that can come about from this special quality of Reiki.

When I was working in the UK I had the opportunity to give a Reiki class to some elderly ladies at a council-run home in Wandsworth, London. The women were all over 70 years old and were suffering from varying degrees of dementia and Alzheimer's disease. After the class, the nurses reported that the more able women had noticeably more energy and purpose and, best of all, that they were giving Reiki to their less able friends.

This quality makes Reiki very different from many other energy healing methods, for example *Chi Gung* (*Qigong*) healing, in which *Chi* (which is believed to be the life energy of the body) needs to be built up within the healer and then pumped into the person to be healed, dispelling their negative *Chi*. This leaves the *Chi Gung* Master depleted of energy. Reiki has the opposite effect in that, after treatment, practitioners often feel rejuvenated themselves having absorbed some of the energy that has been flowing through them to the other person. It is a significant benefit of Reiki that, by giving Reiki to another, you also receive it yourself. It also means that no matter how sick you are, you can still begin rebuilding your own energy without relying solely on others.

Choosing a Reiki Master who's right for you

Once you decide to become a Reiki practitioner – even if it is only to treat yourself, and your family and friends – you have some practical decisions to make: Who's the best Reiki Master for you? What is the best type of class for you to attend?

The following tips will hopefully help you make some of these decisions. Note, these suggestions are based on the Usui System of Reiki as this is my area of expertise.

Trust your intuition

There are many Reiki Masters to choose from and it is important to consider aspects other than simply who is the closest or cheapest. Meet them, talk to them. Do you like this person? Do you feel a connection? The most important criteria for selecting a Reiki Master is that he or she feels right for you.

It is surprising how often the 'right' Reiki Master will appear at the right time and in the right place. I have had so many students say to me, "What a coincidence. I've been thinking about Reiki for years but never enrolled in a course, and then I saw your brochure and just *had* to come to this talk".

All of us come to Reiki with a different perspective, a different life journey and at a different stage in our own personal development. Every Reiki Master has a unique energy and a unique way of activating Reiki in you. There is no good, better, best about it. Every Reiki Master contributes to the global Reiki pool by providing their own specialism. For example, I teach in a grounded, 'down to earth' way and tend to attract business-like people or people who are entering the holistic world for the first time – I seem to provide comfort in the fact I am not too 'weird'! Other Reiki Masters I know and deeply respect provide a more etheric approach to the Reiki they teach – they don't necessarily provide manuals, they prefer to 'feel' the energy rather than discuss it, and they may attract people already well versed in holistic methodology and looking for something totally experiential.

Length of training

Some courses are run over a few hours, others over several days.

What is the difference in the knowledge you will receive at the end? That is a question that may be worth asking. Reiki Masters come from many different lineages and training backgrounds and their courses reflect this diversity. There is also a large difference in the way the applications of Reiki are taught (especially at Level Two and above). Some teachers will also include other aspects of healing such as meditation, crystals, or yoga.

Range of pricing

As you may be aware, there is a huge disparity in the pricing of Reiki courses; ranging from free to exorbitant! Pricing has more to do with the Reiki Master's preference than the actual quality of the Reiki teaching. Reiki in itself is free, as Universal Life Energy we have no right to 'sell' it. However each Reiki Master has had to invest time and/or money in order to train to become a Master, and for many it is their main source of income.

Some Reiki Masters also have additional expenses, such as marketing costs, venue costs and co-ordinator costs to cover. It would seem fair that a Reiki Master teaching at a health centre or classroom charges more than a Reiki Master teaching from home. Some Reiki Masters feel strongly that their time and energy should be free, whilst others feel that their time and energy is a valuable commodity and as such there should be an exchange.

The Reiki Master's philosophy

You are hitting the age-old question when you ask your prospective Reiki Master: "Where does Reiki energy originate from?" The answer you receive will be as varied as the different spiritual philosophies that abound. What does your Reiki Master think? If you can connect with the Reiki Master's philosophy and passion you will be in for a fun seminar. Go to a devoutly Christian Reiki Master as a stoic atheist and you are in for a hard weekend. Some Reiki Masters teach with no philosophical bias, others have a strong one, choose the one which best meets your needs.

Remember that Reiki itself does not have a doctrine or

philosophy as it is neutral, pure energy, but all teachers have their own philosophical beliefs that always find their way into the teaching style and course material. Usui, Hayashi and Takata all had their own 'flavour' and beliefs and Reiki teaching continues to evolve daily. There is no 'better' philosophy that will make the Reiki work more strongly or more effectively, so take care when approaching Masters who claim they have the 'real' Reiki or the 'strongest' attunement.

Why you need a Reiki Master

Please don't try to learn Reiki by yourself out of a book or through the internet. Getting an attunement from a qualified Reiki Master is still an essential part of Reiki training. I am very open to the possibility that this may change. In fact I have seen a growing number of children develop Reiki–type abilities all by themselves. My daughter has had Reiki since she was a baby despite the fact I never consciously attuned her. In her case I believe she received her attunement whilst in utero, as I was still teaching while I was pregnant with her. My feeling is that she simply resonated with my Reiki and 'took' an attunement for herself. Smart kid! However, most of us do not possess knowledge that allows us to self-attune, and this is why we need a Reiki Master.

Accessing Reiki through attunement

The traditional way of accessing Reiki energy is via an 'attunement'. The concept is much like resonance. If we place two same-frequency tuning forks in a room and hit one of the forks with a mallet, the other fork will vibrate in resonance. If we stop the sound resonating from the original fork by placing our hands around it to stop its vibration we will still hear the sound resonating from the second fork – the one that was not touched. This is because vibrations flow through the air from one tuning fork to the other via sound waves, and the second fork responds by resonating to the same vibration.

In a similar way, Reiki Masters are trained to gain access to a vibration that allows the Reiki to activate in them and, via resonance, this vibration is passed on to another person through the ritual of attunement. Over the years Reiki attunement has undergone many changes to the extent that one attunement process differs vastly from another across the teaching lineages. Whatever the process entails, however, the intention is simply to raise the vibration to a level that allows the body to resonate with the same frequency of energy as Reiki. Once this is achieved the body remembers this frequency for life. Likewise, after attunement, funnelling or channelling Reiki becomes a life-long ability (much like learning to ride a bike: once you 'know' something you cannot 'unknow' it).

Anyone can be attuned; there is no talent required or special healing 'gift', I have attuned little children, cats and dogs, I have attuned sceptics and believers, meditation masters and high-flying business executives. If you want to have Reiki there is nothing to stop you achieving that goal.

Although attunements need to be carried out by a qualified Reiki Master and cannot be learned via a book or the internet, the process does not necessarily have to take place face-to-face. The process can be carried out via a 'distance attunement', as resonance is not dependent on physical connection (as the tuning fork example shows). Also note that once you have been attuned, you will have access to Reiki energy but you will not be able to attune other people to Reiki as only qualified Reiki Masters are trained to do this (see the discussion on the levels of Reiki training in chapter eleven).

Once you are attuned, Reiki will simply flow through your hands automatically and without your direction. You can now give Reiki to yourself, and others.

Usui Reiki Level One

At its most basic level, a Reiki Level One course should:

  a. activate the Reiki in your hands permanently via attune-
      ments (also called initiations or activations)
  b. give you enough background information for you to feel

confident in how to use Reiki on both yourself and others

c.   give specific tools and tips for carrying out an effective Reiki treatment.

A typical Reiki Level One course will teach the theory and practical applications of Reiki: the background and history of Reiki, how to use Reiki, how to treat yourself, how to treat others, some tips and pointers as to how to extend your Reiki practice, and other techniques that may be useful to your overall experience of Reiki.

Some Reiki Masters will add extras on to this basic theory and practical information. For instance, they may include crystals, chakra cleansing, bells, prayer, coaching modules, additional rituals, etc. My classes tend to be 'packaged' with discussion about energy and the science of health, as this is my personal interest. As well as the four Level One attunements that connect the student to the Reiki energy, a typical Reiki Level One course run by me would be structured as follows:

1. Introduction to energy

I love talking about energy and how it works in the body. I introduce concepts relating to bioenergetics of the human body; what is seen (physical body) and what is not (the different subtle energy bodies such as *Chi* and *chakras*), and how Reiki works at different levels.

2. Introduction to Reiki

I extend on the theory of how Reiki works and its dynamics. Primarily, I focus on giving a plausible model of how Reiki flows through the body and how it manages to achieve such incredible results so simply.

3. Introduction to chakras

This segment of the course looks at chakras from the Reiki perspective and how the different levels of chakra energy effectiveness can affect the body and mind (this is discussed further in chapter nine).

4. Self treatment

A discussion about why self-Reiki is so important and what to expect from regular self treatment. It is at this point in the course that I teach the basic 12 hand positions and some simple variations on these.

5. Treating others

In this part of the course I discuss the ethics and code of conduct that Reiki practitioners should adhere to whilst treating others either with Reiki first aid or full body treatments. I also cover practical tips aimed to enhance the comfort and overall experience for both the practitioner and the person receiving Reiki during a treatment. Finally, I offer some simple guidelines to equip students to deal effectively with frequently asked questions about Reiki.

6. Additional uses

A discussion about other uses and benefits of Reiki, of which there are many.

7. History

The history of Reiki is not set in stone and many variations of it exist. During this part of the course I discuss the origins of Usui Reiki and the roles of the three people who were key to shaping Reiki as we know it today.

8. Usui's Five Principles

Usui left us with five key principles which can be applied to life as well as to Reiki. To conclude the course I present these principles for consideration (Usui's Five Principles are listed in chapter five.).

Every Master will teach differently and in no way is my course structure definitive. It reflects my own personal interest and approach to teaching. My purpose in outlining the content of my own Reiki Level One course is simply so that you have something to compare against when interviewing prospective Reiki Masters.

Chapter 7

The Reiki Treatment

"Techniques are fingers
pointing to the moon. They are
tools and not to be confused with
the 'real thing'. YOU are the real
thing. YOU are the moon and not
the finger pointing to it"

Frank Arjava Petter, *The Spirit of Reiki*

In the following chapters we look at the ways Reiki energy can be applied. In other words, how we can use Reiki to heal ourselves and what to expect from the different treatment techniques available to us.

The first technique we will focus on is self-Reiki. When we treat others the same principles apply as for self-Reiki, but there are also some ethics to be considered, which are discussed later in this chapter. The term 'self-Reiki', means giving yourself a Reiki treatment in a formal, dedicated way. This technique requires regular, consistent application and allows us to heal via all the pathways available: via the energy pump pathway giving our cells increased access to vital energy and via access and stimulation to the 'peace' centres in our brain, allowing Reiki energy to affect the brain in positive ways (similar to meditation).

This technique requires no effort on the part of the practitioner, but certainly requires the discipline of making time. Ultimately, the more time and dedication that goes into your Reiki, the more you will benefit from it.

The 12 basic positions

The 12 positions can be likened to a recipe; the more comfortable you get with the technique the more you can improvise on the recipe (by altering the hand positions for instance). At a basic level, the technique involves a total of 12 hand positions: four on the head, four on the front of the body and four on the back of the body.

The exact hand positions are not important, and in some traditions many more hand positions are taught. The purpose of the 12 positions is just to cover all the main areas of the body as systematically as possible. Variations can be introduced into the 'recipe' if you have specific physical problems you want to treat – for example, a problem with one of your legs.

Graphical illustrations of these hand positions are not included here as I want to encourage you to feel free to find your own comfortable 'recipe' and not to be restricted by rules. It is understood that Usui, the founder of Reiki, did not use specific hand positions but rather relied on intuition to place his hands in the right place. He would leave his hands in any given position for up to half an hour if he felt it was necessary.

The following suggestions will help you treat your (or someone else's) body in a systematic way, and I invite you to modify and extend as you wish.

Four head positions:
1. Over the eyes/cheeks
2. Top of the head

3. Back of the head
4. Throat/back of neck

Four front positions:
1. Across the chest/nipples
2. Across the ribs
3. Abdomen
4. Groin/reproductive organs

Four back positions:
1. Top of shoulders
2. Shoulder blades (you will need to hug yourself for this one!)
3. Lower back
4. Buttocks

Treatment tips

I suggest the following tips to make self-Reiki treatments more comfortable: you do not need to be lying prone on your back but can move your position to get comfortable. I often begin self-Reiki on my side in foetal position with a pillow in between my elbows to support my hands as I place them on my eyes. I find the more I can support my hands or arms, the easier it is to relax and enjoy the process. If you are finding any position painful then I strongly suggest you modify it to suit your comfort level. Also note that Reiki energy flows from both the palm and the back of the hand, so while giving Reiki to your back, you can lie on the back of your hands without twisting them uncomfortably.

If you fall asleep with your hands still in place, the Reiki will continue to benefit you throughout the night, but I would suggest that you move your hands if you wake up at any stage. If you find you only get through the first four head positions before falling asleep every night, try starting with the front or back body positions on consecutive nights so that you give yourself a full body treatment over the course of the week.

Ideally each of these positions should be held for five minutes, so that the total treatment will last an hour. Some people do find this time commitment a daunting prospect, but if it can be built into a regular night-time or morning routine, it is quite manageable. It is also worth noting that an hour of Reiki gives far greater benefits than one hour of sleep, so by going to bed at your usual time and introducing an hour of Reiki before you go to sleep, you will notice that your day is better for it. There is no need, in other words, to find an 'extra' hour, you simply replace an hour's sleep with Reiki. For those who suffer from sleeping difficulties, practising Reiki at night can be welcomed as a calming routine. Indeed, it is very possible that you will drift off to sleep well before you have completed your hour's treatment. Perfect proof that Reiki is a great treatment for insomniacs!

Props like Reiki music CDs with bells that sound every five minutes, alerting you that it is time to change hand position, are ideal to help you stay relaxed yet focused (recommendations are included in the Resource section of this book).

Learning how to relax

Newcomers to Reiki (especially those who have not meditated before), will probably take some time before they feel themselves falling into a state of meditation. Obviously this will vary from person to person, but the vast majority of people will experience a deep sense of calm and connectedness after 20 minutes of Reiki treatment.

When beginning a self-Reiki treatment it is not necessary to direct your thoughts; just acknowledge them, without trying to change them. Simply find a comfortable resting position and allow the minutes to flow by. At first you may feel restless, anxious, even irritated to be lying still. Notice this, and notice the thinking that goes along with it – the brain that never sleeps! Your thinking cannot impede the flow of Reiki.

As you move to the second position after five minutes, you

might notice that your thoughts become more restful and you may feel yourself becoming more relaxed. Again, whether this does or does not happen is not the point; your aim is simply to notice and acknowledge what is going on inside you. Welcome to your inner life!

As you turn your attention inwards you may be shocked at what you find. Sometimes novice practitioners find self-Reiki quite distressing to begin with and report feeling restless, anxious, angry or agitated. I recommend that if this happens, you recognize it as an urgent message telling you to keep going. Ignoring the body's signals and stopping self-Reiki because of negative reactions is counter-productive. After a few months of self-Reiki, most students report that such reactions simply go away.

As well as emotional responses, some people also experience physical responses; for example, shortness of breath, palpitations, jerking and shaking, sweating or cold shivers, fever and flu. These are a sign of deepening self-awareness. Allow the Reiki to keep flowing through these disruptions and you will soon find your body brings itself back into balance. Of course, any serious disruptions that continue after your treatment has finished should be brought to the attention of your physician immediately as Reiki can also help to highlight symptoms of a more severe ailment which should not be ignored. It should be noted that, although I highlight these incidents, they are uncommon.

After 15 to 20 minutes of Reiki treatment, most people report feeling deeply relaxed and calm. They report much less brain 'chatter' and many will also feel sensations in their hands or body (or both). However, regardless of whether you feel these sensations, you are still receiving Reiki energy. If you feel nothing during your treatments but notice more vitality and energy afterwards, or that you are sleeping better, feel more rested or any other change in your well-being and energy levels – take this as your own sign that your healing has begun. The sensations are obviously a useful validation that something is happening, but not having sensations does not mean nothing is happening. The truth is in what you notice in yourself, and not what you experience during the hour you are receiving Reiki energy.

Most importantly, when you start practising Reiki, try to stick to the one hour treatment protocol. This gives you 20 minutes to reach a deep state of relaxation and at least 40 minutes of deep meditation. *The meditation state is the goal of this process* as it allows the body to rest fully. It is a time when your chattering mind is not barking orders, a time when your cells can get on with their job unimpeded, and a time when subconscious or intuitive help can rise.

There have been many instances when, during my one hour self-Reiki, I have had such a powerful 'ah-ha' moment that it has shifted my perception forever. In some cases niggling problems have been easily solved, and in others deep anguish has been 'blown out of the water'. It's a time of deep healing on all levels.

Remember this is your time to help your body switch back into growth mode, into vitality and your natural state of being. Taking this time is not a luxury, it is critical to your well-being and health.

> *"I had chronic pain from a ruptured disk for 17 years, but it virtually disappeared after I learned Reiki and began regular daily self-care practice. But that's not the most significant change: my regular Reiki has transformed me so that I don't waste as much energy on worry or anger and I try to focus on the present moment. I'm happier and healthier as a result."* Janet

As you continue to practise self-Reiki, it may take less and less time to reach a state of meditation. You may notice that eventually you can drop into meditation as soon as you place your hands on your face, and you may make a decision to shorten your session to 30 or 40 minutes and still experience the same benefits as your original 60-minute session. As this is a recipe and not a mandate, it is up to you to find what works and what fits into your lifestyle (without short-changing yourself!).

> *"I was in a terrible horse riding accident this summer, which resulted in a fractured spleen (which was removed), five broken ribs,*

and head injuries. My recovery – both physical and emotional – was facilitated in miraculous ways by my daily Reiki practice (hours a day as I lay in bed) as well as additional Reiki from friends." Pam

Paying attention to results

Reiki energy is *used by* the body as opposed to *acting on* the body. This means that Reiki energy cannot harm the body in any way and is the main reason why it has gained more acceptance in the medical community; Reiki is seen as an aid to healing and not just another complication to take care of.

However, it is important to ask yourself, or someone you are treating, "what would happen if I (or my client) suddenly improved dramatically?" For instance, if you are on carefully monitored medication, would it create a problem or a situation where you need to check your dosage levels?

In my first year of practicing Reiki my eyesight improved 25% but I ended up with eyestrain because I didn't realize until much later that my lenses were too strong. I have also seen people's cholesterol levels plummet, high blood pressure drop and thyroid and diabetic conditions improve after using Reiki – all of these conditions require regular monitoring by a qualified health care provider. In all these cases it is important to make your doctor aware of your Reiki treatments.

Some Reiki Masters warn against treating the body during surgery or before bones have been set. I have had experience of morphine wearing off quicker than normal while performing Reiki treatments on clients in great pain, and other case studies suggest that the application of anaesthesia may be complicated when mixed with Reiki. One explanation is that the body is finding its own balance and the drug is seen as a toxin and so is expelled by the body more quickly and efficiently than expected. Obviously this is not a helpful efficiency when undergoing surgery!

However, some surgeons and anaesthetists prescribe Reiki during operations, and with very positive effects. Libby Barnett and Maggie Chambers detail many case studies in their book *Reiki, Energy Medicine* (p.58):

> *"Because universal life force always works for the highest healing good, and the patient's cells are in charge of the amount received, Reiki never interferes with anesthesia, nor is there any concern about overdose."* Page 58

Barnett and Chambers specialise in working with doctors and training nurses and so have a great deal of experience in using Reiki in a medical setting. Certainly more research is needed in this area and my own preference is to give Reiki before and after surgery as a 'just in case' measure. Overall, my experience has been that Reiki works to enhance medication and reduce side-effects and that the body uses the energy intelligently and positively.

It is also possible that when Reiki energy stimulates our bodies to heal other reactions might be noticed that seem 'bad' to our linear minds. When we go to the doctor we usually expect to be prescribed something that will make us feel better by ridding us of troublesome symptoms. Reiki, on the other hand, works on the underlying *cause* of the problem, which can often result in an *increase* of 'symptoms' as the body works through the necessary healing process – making us feel worse rather than better. As we discussed previously, these symptoms or side effects may take the form of headaches, stomach upsets, irregular/abnormal bowel movements, increased heat, tingling or pain in the body, and more emotional sensitivity such as crying, anger or anxiety. Although these side effects can be disconcerting, they are good signs that the Reiki is helping your body shift and heal. The more you self-Reiki, the more energy your body has to work on the issue and the faster it will get back into balance. You can never 'over-Reiki' yourself or someone else. If you get to a state of equilibrium, the Reiki energy will no longer be drawn into the body and the flow will simply stop by itself.

If you are treating someone else and they have an adverse

reaction, it is recommended you follow up with another treatment as soon as possible until the symptoms subside. Although these symptoms are a natural process of the body healing they can be disturbing to experience and it is important to provide reassurance.

Treating others using the 12 basic positions

Giving someone a full Reiki treatment has many benefits – both for the giver and the receiver of the Reiki. Such a treatment is symbiotic, in that both participants receive some form of healing. Reiki practitioners report feeling calmer, better, less stressed after they have given Reiki to someone else.

If you want others to really benefit from Reiki, please do bear in mind that by encouraging them to learn Reiki for themselves you will ultimately be giving them the best help of all. This way they can begin their own healing journey through daily Reiki self-treatments. The Reiki Centre Survey shows clearly that improvement in any condition is generally related to the amount of Reiki being received. If self-Reiki is not possible, I recommend a minimum of three treatments from a qualified practitioner within the first week, and then at least one treatment a week until the issue is resolved.

Tips and ethics when treating others

When giving someone a Reiki treatment the environment should be as relaxing and calming as possible: remember the point of a full hour's treatment is to induce an alpha or meditation state as this provides optimal healing on all levels, promoting the client's growth mode to flick back on and encouraging their immune system to work more efficiently.

It is preferable that both the person receiving the Reiki and the Reiki practitioner wear non-synthetic clothing during the treatment. The Reiki itself is not impeded, but the body's own energy or *Chi* moves less fluidly through synthetic materials. Some people may also experience a 'prickling' against synthetic materials (like static) which makes the treatment process uncomfortable.

Suggest to your client that they may wish to remove restrictive clothing (eg belts, ties, corsets, nylons/ tights, wire-cupped bras) in order to be more comfortable and relaxed. The body is often in a state of heightened awareness during a session and such restrictions may feel uncomfortable and distracting.

Ask your client whether they prefer a pillow for their head and, whenever possible, place a pillow under their knees while they are lying face up (to protect their lower back). This, of course, depends on the condition of the person you are treating. A pregnant woman, for example, often finds it easier to lie on her side during treatment. No specific treatment position is required so take comfort into consideration and adapt the treatment accordingly.

Often when I go to the hospital to treat friends or clients with Reiki, hand positions are restricted by equipment or the nature of the person's illness or injury. In these circumstances, just aim to cover off as many of the 12 positions as you practically can.

Music played during a Reiki treatment should preferably be calming with a non-specific beat and no vocals, as this might distract from the treatment. Do what you can to ensure that telephones will not interrupt your session and that you will not be otherwise disturbed. If the treatment takes place in someone else's home or environment request that similar measures are taken so that your session will be uninterrupted.

Before beginning treatment, explain that it is preferable that your client focuses inwardly and tries to forget about you, and that talking or discussion is left until after the treatment (unless they need to communicate something about the session itself – for example, that they are not lying comfortably).

The treatment involves placing your hands, for five minutes, in each of the 12 positions listed above. You may place your hands gently and directly on the person being treated (there is no need to apply pressure) or, if preferred, hover about two or three inches above their body. Either way the Reiki energy will flow through your hands and into them.

Although there is no requirement to guide Reiki energy in any way, Usui was thought to begin every healing session with a short meditation and prayer. He would then intuitively place his hands over the parts of the body that he felt required healing and finish with what is termed 'dry bathing', a technique to disconnect from the other persons energy. I encourage you to experiment with both the prayer and the disconnection techniques to see if they serve you, a more thorough explanation of 'dry bathing' is given later in this chapter.

Getting permission

It is also prudent here to emphasize that it is NOT OK to Reiki someone without his or her permission. This is not purely for ethical reasons. Although Reiki is always safe, it can have dramatic effects that might impact the person's well-being in other ways. When you melt someone's iceberg all the flotsam and jetsam trapped in the ice also surfaces. As mentioned earlier in this chapter, while some people simply release and have no direct knowledge of the changes, others go through a cathartic response that may include strong emotions and physical reactions. If this happens to someone and they do not know why it is happening (because they don't know that you are giving them Reiki) it can be frightening. It may seem a joke to state that some people are happy in their misery, but it is not for us to judge the level of misery of others, or to decide to change things for them.

Reiki can sometimes have serious and dramatic effects that can be hard to imagine, especially if your own experience of Reiki has been gentle. I once received an email from a woman half way around the world struggling to make sense of what had just happened to her. She had been to a beauty salon earlier that day where the beautician offered her five minutes of Reiki. Without really knowing what it was, she agreed. After only a few minutes she felt an immense sadness well up and overpower her, so much so that she started sobbing uncontrollably. The beautician was not knowledgeable enough about Reiki to offer her any support or explanation, so the woman left the salon, still crying.

Three hours later she found me through the Internet and, still crying, emailed me to try to find out what was going on. Through our ensuing conversations she came to see her emotional release as positive and healing. To my own mind, however, her experience was frightening and unnecessary and should have originally been handled with much more sensitivity and care.

When you give someone Reiki please always carry a sense of responsibility. As the channeller of this extraordinary energy you can have a major impact on the lives around you. If you start giving a treatment and your client bursts into tears or has some form of emotional release, it is your responsibility to stay with them until their release has passed. This may mean your five-minute treatment turns into an hour, or your hour treatment turns into a two hour treatment, or you may need to arrange a prompt follow up treatment.

Obviously, in your day-to-day contact with people you are passing on small gifts of Reiki all the time, but these are not of a significant quantity to be of note. I also leave it to you to decide the ethics of providing Reiki to someone who is unconscious or unable to give you specific permission, as in the case of an emergency. In my own value system I have always helped where I can – with or without permission – in an emergency situation. I feel the benefits of Reiki far outweigh any of the potential negative side effects. Someone suffering from severe shock is unlikely to notice a headache or upset stomach as a result of the energy pouring into their system. But this is a personal choice and I tend to follow my intuition on a case-by-case basis.

The key is to remain clear on your intention, are you truly trying to help someone or are you trying to 'improve' them? My definition of helping someone is that they themselves will perceive a benefit from what you are doing, whereas in trying to 'improve' someone, I notice that my intention is sometimes to make them more acceptable – to me! If you find that you are trying to 'improve' someone else, you should perhaps turn your thoughts to yourself instead as that is often where the 'improvement' is most needed!

Let me illustrate this. For a short while, I volunteered at a home for severely handicapped children. The Reiki volunteers were given a roster by the head nurse and we did not have the freedom to treat other patients in the ward. The first time I went I was struck by how eager some of the patients were to have a Reiki treatment; they seemed so happy to see us. I was also shocked to notice that one or two of the children we tried to help would be lying passively on the beds but quickly began to twist and turn, as if in discomfort, once we started treating them. One little girl began to cry every time I placed my hands near her, and then stopped and went back to her passive state when I moved my hands away. It seemed she was giving me a very clear message to 'go away'. I spoke to the head volunteer and the nurse, suggesting that we focus on the children who obviously enjoyed receiving Reiki and respected the wishes of others who didn't. Unfortunately, the nurse's attitude was that the patients that she pinpointed 'needed' the most healing. She was looking at it from a purely medical point of view, which was understandable given her situation. However, from my perspective, I could not convince myself that I truly had these children's permission and as a result I chose to drop out of the programme.

I have no idea why most of the children loved it, yet some did not. I have no idea what kind of icebergs these children had, or what they experienced during Reiki that they found uncomfortable. My job was to respond to their requests with respect, and not judgement.

Protecting yourself

Theories are divided about whether or not practitioners should protect themselves against energy depletion during a Reiki treatment. My own Reiki Master was very clear that when you Reiki someone, the energy is flowing only one-way; from your hands into the recipient. As a result, such protection is unnecessary.

Over the years, however, I have found that some circumstances – and some people – can leave me feeling very drained of energy. What is important here is to realize that it is not the Reiki that is draining you, but a personal energy interplay that is going on – one that would happen regardless of whether or not you are giving that person a Reiki treatment.

To explain this further, think about how you feel after spending time with a particularly demanding friend – one who complains a lot or is always very negative. Chances are you will feel drained and tired, as though that person has somehow 'sucked the life' out of you. Alternatively, maybe you are the negative one, and when you spend time with your more positive friends you walk away feeling vitalised and energised yourself. Either way, there is a personal interplay of energy resources going on every day, depending on who we spend our time with.

If you are particularly empathic and tend to feel drained after giving Reiki to others you can choose to either stop giving treatments until your own energy field is more robust, or you can try some of the protection techniques taught by many energy healers. Personally, if I have had a particularly emotional session with someone I find that a cleansing shower works best for me.

Other protection methods I have tried in the past include a 'karate chop' which is simply a slicing motion with your hands across your chest as if to sever any links, or a flicking of your wrists as if to remove surplus water. Remember these techniques are symbolic so just try a few out and then choose the one that seems to work for you.

Beginnings and endings – the Usui way

It is understood that Usui's treatments started with a prayer or meditation (this could last for 20 minutes). I invite students to experiment with 'gassho', which means 'two hands coming together' and is an excellent way to centre and focus yourself before you begin a treatment on others.

Simply place your hands in prayer pose in front of your chest and you can either focus on your hands for a few breaths or silently ask Reiki to flow to the highest good of the person in front of you (or any other meaningful prayer). This is not a necessary part of Reiki but many of my students enjoy the ritual and find it a good way to bring reverence or respect into what they are doing.

Usui would then begin Reiki healing by intuitively placing his hands on his patients. He would complete the session with a simple 'Dry Bathing' technique[24] to symbolically disconnect from the treatment or signal the end of the treatment. The 'Dry Bathing' technique is carried out as follows:

1. Bring your right hand to the left side of your chest, over the collarbone. Stroke down gently across your chest to the right hip.
2. Repeat with left hand across the right side of your chest to the left hipbone.
3. Repeat motion with your right hand.
4. Now use your right hand and gently stroke your left wrist over the open palm of your left hand past the fingertips.
5. Use your left hand to stroke the right palm.
6. You may repeat again with right hand.

It is part of your own discovery of Reiki healing to experiment and even develop your own techniques or merge techniques that you already use into your practice. And if all this talk of protection and safety and commitment is daunting, remember that Reiki is designed as a self-treatment therapy and as such there is no need to feel obligated to give Reiki to others if you do not feel ready.

This said, many of us do wish to use Reiki to help those around us. Having a young family I am often grateful that I have Reiki in my hands. It has brought me great comfort to know I can do something to help – especially in an emergency situation. Treating someone else with Reiki is also the best way to open that person to learning it himself or herself: it is unlikely I would have discovered Reiki had my mother not given me that first treatment and for that I am truly grateful.

Treating children

I love teaching children about Reiki; their innocent, open minds are unburdened by rigid belief systems and, in general, they call a spade a spade. When I ask children to describe what they feel during the attunement process they effortlessly come up with colourful adjectives. Children respond wonderfully to Reiki and because they have no pre-conceptions or doubts they also feel Reiki very strongly. Younger children may find the energy too 'hot' and may not have the patience for a long session, so the general rule of thumb is to modify the basic 12 positions and Reiki children only with as many hand positions as are required to give good overall coverage of their bodies.

For example, a small baby may only need five minutes of Reiki as, by placing one hand on the baby's front and one on its back, you will have pretty much covered its entire body.

As the child gets bigger you may manage one head position and one body position (ten minutes in total), then maybe one head, one front, one back position (15 minutes total). Even up to the age of 12 you'll be lucky to get a child to lie still for more than 20 minutes!

However, every child is different and it's important to respect their wishes (even if you think you know best!). My own children illustrate this perfectly:

My eldest has been a Reiki fan since birth (and possibly even before that: she used to kick with glee when I placed my hands on my belly). She is very comfortable with the energy and gives herself Reiki as well as asking for it from me when she feels she needs an extra boost. Her instructions to me are very clear and she tells me when she wants it, and when she's had sufficient. As a result of being a 'Reiki baby' she has never been on antibiotics, has had fevers less than a handful of times, has never been off school sick, and heals at a remarkable rate when she falls over or suffers the usual childhood scrapes and bumps. She is literally the embodiment of what Reiki looks like in a child.

My youngest is quite the opposite. Ever since she was a baby she found Reiki hot, bothersome and uncomfortable. If she got sick I was not allowed to put my hands on her body; if she fell over my hands had to stay a respectful distance away. This is also a common reaction; luckily it does tend to diminish as children grow older and their energy systems mature (she is quite amenable to Reiki now that she is six). As a result, although still a healthy child, she has been on the usual rounds of antibiotics, allergy medication, occasional asthma attacks, and her knocks and bumps take weeks instead of days to heal. My very own 'control' in the Reiki experiment!

"I have seen significant improvement in my autistic son's behaviour and moods. So much so, that he knows to ask for Reiki when he feels an angry mood coming on." Robin

"Whenever I give Reiki to my children or their friends it is amazing how they react. Seconds later they are calm and stop crying." Beate

The night of my Reiki Level One attunement, my one-year-old nephew was teething and was very upset. I was cuddling him and he grabbed my hand and put it on his cheek. I stroked it and then moved it and he grabbed it and pushed it hard to his cheek and left his hand there to keep mine still. Then he drifted off to sleep quickly. He will still grab for my hand when, for example, he falls and hurts his knee." Anonymous

Chapter 8

Topical and First Aid Treatment

"We can do no great things, only small things with great love."

Mother Teresa

Harnessing the energy pump pathway, we can use Reiki to provide first aid healing treatment to help heal physical injuries and emergencies. The benefits of this Reiki technique are recognised in hospitals, emergency rooms, and by an increasing number of surgeons and doctors.

Dr Mehmet Oz of TV fame (and a leading cardiovascular surgeon in the USA), welcomes Reiki in his operating theatres. Says Dr Oz, "Reiki has become a sought-after healing art among patients and mainstream medical professionals." In January 2010 on *The Dr Oz Show*, he quotes energy medicine as being "ultimately the most important alternative medicine treatment of all…".

Nancy Eos, a Doctor and Reiki Master, has written a book, *Reiki and Medicine*, describing her experiences with Reiki in the Emergency Room. "I can't imagine practicing medicine without

Reiki," Eos says. "With Reiki all I have to do is touch a person. Things happen that don't usually happen. Pain lessens in intensity. Rashes fade. Wheezing gives way to breathing clearly. Angry people begin to joke with me."

When we use Reiki as an energy pump and place our hands on a specific area of the body that needs physical healing – an injured knee for example – the Reiki energy will flow through our hands to the knee. The faster you can place your hands on the affected area, the faster the healing can begin. So when we talk about 'first aid' Reiki, we're simply talking about putting our hands immediately above, or on, the problem area. This technique is a great aid to physical healing, to providing abundant energy supplies to cells so that they can do their job properly. It gives the cells a boost which is often accompanied by a sensation of heat, tingling or cold as they respond to the new input of energy.

> "I had a serious wipe-out on the ski slopes in Taos a couple of years ago. I lost control coming down the mountain and slammed into a wall of packed snow and ice. I hit so hard I broke the skis. After I discovered that I was still alive (I really wasn't sure at first … I half expected to see Sonny Bono holding out his hand to me…) I got to my feet and, incredulously, walked away – although I did feel like I had been beaten with a baseball bat. When I got back to the house I lay down straightaway and began to give myself Reiki. I drifted in and out of consciousness and when I finally snapped out of it about an hour and a half later, I wondered how I was going to feel when I stood up... if I could stand up. I got up and I felt great. Not an ache, not a pain, not a bruise. I couldn't believe it. The next morning, the same thing. It's like the crash had never happened, and I never had a single repercussion from it, either. It was then that I could finally relate to the term 'Reiki Miracle.' Jim

> "I have found Reiki very helpful for use during acute asthma attacks while waiting for the medicine to take effect; it keeps the passageways open so I can breathe." Anonymous

"Last Christmas, a woman I know asked me to treat her knees which were very painful because of an operation and Baker's cyst. I was not aware of it, but she told me that a year earlier, when I treated her knees with Reiki for half an hour the pain had just disappeared. She had thought of me over the following months, but hesitated to ask for help once more. However, this Christmas the pain had become so unbearable, that she finally phoned me. During the hour I treated her knees again, she felt both cold and warm. She told me later that I 'saved' her Christmas, she didn't even have to use her sticks for a week or two afterwards. Normally she is dependent on these. I have to admit that I was surprised myself." Inger

When we use Reiki for first aid it is important not to consider it as a *replacement* for other first aid tools but as *complementary* to them; I would never condone replacing an established emergency practice with Reiki. As with all things, let common sense prevail.

However, when it comes to minor cuts, accidents, burns, aches and pains, relieving the symptoms of coughs and colds, reducing the itchiness and severity of rashes and minor allergies that one would commonly treat with over-the-counter medicines, I have replaced my first aid kit, or home medicine cabinet, with Reiki. I cannot remember the last time I took medication, pain killers or antibiotics. Even after two caesarean operations I did not need pain killers (to the shock of the nurses on duty!) though note I did have local anaesthesia during the operation!

As well as being a great quick fix for helping bleeding and repair, Reiki is also superb at reducing pain and shock. My daughters know to come running to my hands when they hurt themselves and it is so calming for me to know that the Reiki will help them heal. I cannot remember the amount of times I have been grateful to have Reiki when faced with the usual falls and accidents in the playground.

In Reiki first aid treatments we are simply responding to our body's aches and pains and ailments in a supportive and nurturing

way. Placing your hands on or over the pain or injury is enough
to activate the flow of Reiki and begin your healing. You can
experiment with how long you need to hold the position: normally
I would recommend between 15 and 40 minutes, depending on
the pain being experienced (many practitioners simply keep their
hands in place until the pain goes away or diminishes sufficiently).

*"When I was brand new to Reiki, my girlfriend slammed the
car door on her thumb. It was completely black and very swollen.
I held her hand for several minutes and voila! No more pain, no
discolouring, no swelling. It sure made a believer of me."* Patsy

*"I gave Reiki to a person who had chest pain. After half an
hour he stood up and felt well enough to hike with his wife from a
snow-bound mountain lodge to the hospital emergency room. The
doctor could not believe that he survived a full blown heart attack."*
Anonymous

*"My son had brain surgery to remove a tumour that was
causing many problems. He asked me to give him Reiki after his
surgery while he was in ICU recovery. His blood pressure was very
high and they were worried about it. I began the session. The other
visitors in the room were watching and, as the session began, one
noticed that my son's heart rate and blood pressure went down on
the monitor he was attached to. They signalled silently to me to
look at the monitor. My son had no idea about the monitor; he was
just sitting in the bed with his eyes closed, welcoming the energy. A
nurse interrupted me and his readings went up. When I continued,
the readings went down and stayed down. The readings were giving
me physical proof that the Reiki was working. The nurses were not
surprised when we told them what we saw, since they had already
experienced what Reiki could do for their patients. My son went
home sooner than the doctors thought he would. They said he was
healing extraordinarily well."* Linda

As when treating yourself with first aid Reiki, the faster you can treat someone else's injuries the better. Bear in mind that for many physical injuries, Reiki can create a significant increase in activity around the wound that can intensify the pain felt (particularly true of burn cases). In these instances it is always good to warn people that it might hurt more for a while but then will feel much better. Children especially may not have patience for more pain when you Reiki a burn for them.

Tips when using Reiki first aid

For bleeding: you will notice a much faster response to blood clotting and sealing of the wound (please be sensible, if it requires stitches or is bleeding profusely, go to the emergency room immediately and Reiki on the way!). If you are giving Reiki to someone else you might place your hands above the wound instead of directly on the wound, Reiki is also equally effective through surgical gloves.

A friend of mine is a great cook and always takes over the kitchen when he comes to dinner. One evening he was chopping vegetables when he sliced his finger on a knife. It was not a bad or deep cut but it was bleeding quite freely so I offered to Reiki it. He agreed and we stood chatting while I held his finger for about five minutes, after which time he was surprised to see the bleeding had not only stopped, but the cut had healed over already. As someone who regularly cuts himself during kitchen mishaps, he was well aware of the usual healing time of his body, he told me it was "like magic"!

For minor burns: you may notice an increase in intensity of pain and then a quick release of that pain. In my own experience a quick response to minor burns will help prevent water blisters and encourage almost miraculous healing.

On my thirtieth birthday I created a perfect Reiki experiment by lifting a tray of sausage rolls out of the oven and burning the tops of both my thumbs on the oven door, the burns were identical in size and position. I spent the rest of the evening with my right hand on my left-hand burn, and left the other one to heal on its own.

The following morning I was impressed to see that my left thumb, the one that had received the Reiki, was burnt but had suffered no water blister and was not painful – the burn looked like it was about a week old and ready to scab. My right thumb went through the normal healing process by first forming a painful water blister and then scabbing. The difference in healing time between both hands was over a week. Quite incredible.

For breaks: go immediately to the hospital. I have known cases where broken bones have started to respond to Reiki before they have been properly set and realigned, causing incorrect bone growth to complicate matters later on. I recommend waiting until a doctor has correctly set the broken bone before beginning Reiki. If there is a great deal of pain or shock, treat the lower back (the kidneys) or place your hands near but not directly on the affected area.

In my experience, breaks and major injuries that are not healing well often signal a deeper issue at play (in other words, the accident is just the 'tip of the iceberg'). Could it be that your intuition or inner wisdom has engineered a major shock just to get you to stop and listen to what's going on inside you? When you are treating others after a major accident it is sometimes useful to suggest that they reflect on what message their intuition is trying to give them, as the story below illustrates. The same applies if it is you who has had the accident!

I got a call from a woman who was disappointed that her broken leg was not healing as fast as the doctor had expected. This was despite many hours of Reiki both on her leg, and on the rest of her body through self-treatments. I went to give her more Reiki and while I was there we got chatting. I asked her what was going on in her mind at the moment she actually fell, and she told me that she had been thinking she needed to slow down. We both laughed as it would appear her wish had come true!

In this case the only recommendation I had for her was to keep resting and to allow her mind to slow down too so that her entire being could reset and recuperate. Once she accepted that her broken leg was in response to something she needed to take care of internally, her leg began healing normally.

For shock: hands can be applied to the forehead and back of the head to help 'reset' and calm the brain. It also helps with clarity, control and perspective.

In a true emergency (once you have called the appropriate emergency services), Reiki can be a strong help to others. The only issue to consider is getting permission if they are unconscious or not mentally able to communicate with you. In these cases I usually take a judgement call based on the situation, but this is a very personal decision and there is no right or wrong answer. What I find myself doing does not always follow a logical sequence as my body can often move before I have had time to consciously think about it, as the experience below illustrates.

While practicing the 'breath of fire' (a breathing technique) at a yoga class, my hands began to tingle very strongly. A moment later, a woman two mats away from me suddenly started having an epileptic fit. More quickly than I could ever have moved consciously, I leapt over the person next to me and put my hands onto the fitting woman. There was no doubt in my mind that the Reiki had 'activated' before the fit started, and this confirmed to me that I am really just a 'human funnel' for the Reiki energy. Although the woman appeared to be in great distress externally, and people around us were shouting and crying, inside I felt nothing but calm, connected energy, it was a very humbling experience on many levels.

I have experienced many similar incidents of being able to share the gift of Reiki with those around me who are in distress. Often the results are met with amazement, which leads people to become more curious about Reiki and can often open doors in the most unexpected of ways.

I was at a children's party with friends a while ago. My friends come in 'Reiki' and 'non-Reiki' categories, and this party was of the 'non-Reiki' category. One of my friends' children twisted his ankle on the bouncy castle and was literally screaming the place down. Although my hands were itching to grab his poor ankle, experience has taught me to respect other people's business, and so I hovered making cooing sounds and trying to look sympathetic. Mike (the boy's father) tried to calm his screaming child and frantically looked about for help, his eyes settled on me and he blurted out to his son "Don't worry, Elaine's here! She's got Reiki!" I grabbed the little boy's ankle and he stopped crying instantly. Even I was shocked. Mike's jaw hit the floor and I tried to keep mine in check, whilst stifling a giggle. After about five minutes his son, who was chatting happily by now, told his dad he was fine and ran off to join his friends. Mike and I exchanged glances and nothing more was said. Later he told my husband it had been the most amazing thing to witness.

This story not only illustrates the wonderful benefits of having Reiki and being able to, in your own way, lessen pain and suffering in the world, but it also shows what an incredible gift it is to share with others who might not be open to energy healing. Since that incident, Mike's wife has gone on to train as a Jin Shin Jytsu teacher and I like to think that that one little incident may have helped open a door for them both to explore a different world.

A gentle reminder

First aid Reiki is only intended for temporary relief. It is similar, in a sense, to taking a pain killer. We can alleviate the symptoms with it but five minutes of Reiki a day, or having a treatment only when we feel pain, is not going to have any deep effect. You may, for example, be able to alleviate a stuffed up nose and reduce a fever caused by the flu, but you will not be able to build up your immune system to the point where you don't catch the flu in the first place.

I liken it to any form of 'quick fix'. If I want to lose weight to fit into my party dress I might go on a crash diet (first aid Reiki) but if I want to permanently alter my body size, I need to eat healthily every day. For a permanent shift in the way I feel and a sense of wellness and peace from day to day, I need to apply Reiki in a systematic and dedicated way, as described in the previous chapter.

Chapter 9

Chakra Balancing Treatment

"Don't solve your problems, dissolve your problems – so they should not reoccur again."

Yogi Bhajan

The third Reiki technique I'd like to look at is used for chakra balancing. I've included this treatment here as it is an excellent way to balance our internal energy system and also a tremendous stress release. This technique works by pumping Universal Life Energy directly into our spiritual energy centres.

A chakra (the literal Sanskrit translation of which is 'wheel') is a centre of spiritual energy or an expression of consciousness. It is thought that spiritual energy begins its expression here and filters out through the body at certain points, affecting the organs closest to it. If a chakra is not 'optimised' then it can have an adverse effect on the corresponding organs and flow of energy to the chakras above and below it. Higher consciousness is thought to flow through the top of your head down through the energy centres located along your spine and out through your feet, while earth energy is thought to flow up through your feet and up your spine to the top of your head.

There are many instinctive references to this flow of spiritual energy. For instance, we refer to someone who is practical, unassuming and sensible as being 'down to earth' or having their 'feet planted firmly on the ground'; and someone who is an idealist or a dreamer as having their 'head in the clouds'. The chakra points have distinctive characteristics that we may recognise as instinctively true.

The seven chakras

The first chakra (the Base or Root) is located at the base of the spine and represents earth energy. It is our first conscious experience of the physical world around us and is related to self-preservation and physical identity. Reflecting the basic needs of a newborn baby, the Base chakra represents trust as well as concepts of safety and security. It physically affects the legs, pelvis and base of the spine. If this chakra is not balanced or is blocked it can manifest in many issues based on rigidity including constipation (inability to let go), arthritis, sciatica, weakness or problems in the ankles and knees. The body can often be very literal as it translates our energy blockages into physical symptoms. This is the body's way of giving us messages and guiding us towards resolution and solutions by showing us which area we need to energetically unblock. A person with a robust and balanced Base chakra has a deep trust and acceptance in life.

The next chakra (the Sacral) is located below the navel and represents relationships and creativity. If the Base chakra is related to our physical identity, the Sacral chakra is an expression of our emotional identity and dictates our fluidity or movement through life. Our creativity, sensuality and passion flows through this chakra. When it is blocked we may physically manifest issues in the fluids of our body; reproductive organs, kidneys, lymph or circulatory system. A person with a strong and balanced Sacral chakra is creative, sensitive to beauty and emotionally mature.

The third chakra (the Solar Plexus) is located between our ribs, directly over our stomach (which is much higher in our rib cage than most of us realize!) This is the 'power house' chakra and is an expression of our willpower and ego. This chakra manages digestion of both food and life. It gives us our personal strengths, stamina and presence. Any blocks can manifest as digestive problems, stomach ulcers, anger issues or muscle weaknesses. A person with a balanced Solar Plexus chakra is confident, committed and calm.

The fourth chakra (the Heart) is the centre of balance. It is said that when all else is stripped away, only love remains. Certainly our heart is the most powerful organ in our body energetically, giving off more than 100 times more electromagnetic energy than our brains. The Heart chakra is thought to balance and moderate the entire chakra system and is arguably the most important chakra to keep balanced and robust. This chakra is our expression of love, compassion and gratitude. When out of balance or blocked we manifest many of the diseases so common in our modern society: high blood pressure, heart disease, lung problems, and asthma. We also feel fear and worry, our classic protection response symptom. A person with a well balanced Heart chakra is compassionate, unconditionally loving and lives in gratitude.

The fifth chakra (the Throat) is an expression of inner truth. When we are not living or speaking from a place of inner truth we often blame or deny, and the resulting physical symptoms can manifest as stiff neck, sore throat, thyroid issues, or hearing problems as our voice literally struggles to be heard. A person with a strong Throat chakra is authentic, light in humour, and speaks out easily.

The sixth chakra (the Third Eye) is situated just above the eye brows and represents our intuition and inner guidance. We often shut down or block this chakra in favour of our literal left brain functions which results in a lack of clarity of life direction, indecision, depression and physical symptoms such as headaches, eye issues, and nightmares. A person with a well-balanced Third Eye chakra has a strong inner guidance and makes decisions easily and effortlessly.

The final chakra (the Crown chakra) is located at the top of the head and represents universal spirit, or connection to God. Many energy healers who work with chakras believe this chakra does not block easily and is constantly open as our connection to universal spirit is our own life force. However, my own belief is that we often neglect this chakra and feel disconnected from it. As a result we experience boredom, apathy and alienation. Our connection is easily re-established via self-Reiki, allowing us to experience the boundlessness and bliss that accompanies the expression of this final chakra.

The table below outlines the qualities of each chakra. Many people find it fascinating when they recognise a physical ailment and then can see the emotional condition related to it (although they often find it easier to spot the connection in others than in themselves!).

CHAKRA	HEALTHY CHARACTERISTICS	UNHEALTHY CHARACTERISTICS
Base/Root Colour: Red Element: Earth Situated at the base of the spine Affects legs, pelvis, base spine	Acceptance Grounded Stillness Trusting (place in this world)	Resentment Rigidity Stuckness Poor Immune system Pelvic/leg/adrenals/ elimination issues Obesity Constipation, Haemorrhoids Sciatica Degenerative arthritis
Sacral Colour: Orange Element: Water Situated about one inch below the navel Affects reproductive organs, lymph, blood, kidneys, bladder	Creativity Sensuality/sexuality Desire/passion Manage Change/fluid Pleasure/beauty Emotionally grounded Movement/dance Nurturance	Manipulation Guilt Materialism Attachment to method Fridgidity/sexual repression/impotence Reproductive Kidney Uterine Bladder Circulatory system issues Lower back stiffness

Solar Plexus Colour: Yellow Element: Fire Situated in the V of the ribs (over the stomach) Affects digestive system, liver, pancreas	Commitment Will power Humour Energy, stamina Personal Strength Presence Calmness and deepness of breath	Anger Greed Digestive system, Pancreas Liver Muscle issues Ulcers Diabetes Hypoglycaemia Breathing stiff/erratic
Heart Colour: Green Element: Air Situated in the centre of the chest Affects heart, lungs, arms, thymus	Compassion Love Gratitude Acceptance Leaps of Faith	Attachment & fear Worry Thymus Lungs Heart Arms Hands Asthma High blood pressure Heart disease Lung disease
Throat Colour: Blue Element: Ether Situated in the throat Affects throat, neck, shoulders, ears, thyroid	Truth Being 'yourself' Singing, chanting Humour Speaking	Blame Denial Thyroid Parathyroid Sore throat Stiff neck Colds Hearing problems
3rd Eye Colour: Indigo Situated in between the eye brows Affects pituitary, eyes, head	Clarity vision Intuition Strong inner voice Inner guidance Strong decision-making	Indecision Lack vision or purpose Depression Blindness Headaches Nightmares Eyestrain Blurred vision
Crown Colour: Violet Situated at the top of the head Affects pineal, head	Boundlessness Connection to God Bliss	Apathy Boredom Depression Alienation Confusion Lack of will to live

Chakras may block or become less robust for many reasons. For example, if I grew up not being listened to (the 'children-should-be-seen-and-not-heard, or 'only-speak-when-you're-spoken-to' type of upbringing) and have been repeatedly forced into a socially 'acceptable' role that is not the 'real' me, the chances are that over the years I will have slowly shut down my Throat chakra which is connected to communication and truth. If the situation remains unchanged, I may discover I have frequent throat problems, sore neck or thyroid issues. And if the block becomes more severe, it will also spill into the chakras above and below as the energy builds up, causing issues in the Heart and Third Eye chakra.

Hand positions for chakra balancing treatment

The Reiki chakra balancing treatment helps us to release blocked energy. It is carried out by placing our hands over each chakra in turn and allowing Reiki energy to flow for about five minutes. Over time, this treatment will help us feel more balanced, and more 'in flow'.

The accuracy of hand positions is more important in chakra balancing treatments as hands need to be placed directly over the chakra energy points. When performing a chakra balancing treatment on others, move your hands gently over the part of the body where each chakra point is located. Over time, and with increased sensitivity, you should be able to feel 'suction' or a pulling sensation when you hit the correct spot (some people feel a repelling or pulsing sensation). The key is to feel the difference in energy so that you can pin-point the location exactly. It is also interesting to note the different sensations based on each chakra's unique quality; as a rule of thumb they tend to become more 'yang' as they move down the body: it is quite common to feel more heat in the hands over the Base, Sacral and Solar Plexus chakras. The higher chakras (Third Eye and Crown) can often give a feeling of intense tingling in the hands denoting the higher vibrational energy present in these chakras.

As a guide, the hand positions for chakra balancing are described below:

1. **Crown** – directly on the top of the head
2. **Third Eye** – hands should sandwich the forehead and the

base of the skull at the back of the head

3. **Throat** – front and back of neck
4. **Heart** – centre of the chest, parallel to the heart and corresponding back of the chest along the spine
5. **Solar Plexus** – the V of the ribs (over the stomach) and corresponding back of the lower ribs along the spine
6. **Sacral** – about two finger widths below the navel and corresponding lower back along the spine
7. **Base/Root** – base of the body and coccyx, base of the spine.

When giving yourself this treatment, also try to be sensitive to the energy points to ensure you get the maximum benefits, I often combine the hand positions to cover off two chakras at one time, this is much easier than trying to reach behind your back! The treatment positions for this method would be as follows:

1. **Crown & Third Eye** – one hand directly on the top of the head, other hand on the forehead.
2. **Throat & Heart** – one hand on the front of the neck, other hand on the centre of the chest.
3. **Solar Plexus & Sacral** – one hand on the V of the ribs (over the stomach) and other hand about two finger widths below the belly button.
4. **Base** – one hand base of the body and coccyx, other hand on the base of the spine.

Chakra balancing is wonderful as a quick 'pick me up' as it can be done in 35 minutes or less (even holding each position for just three minutes will provide benefits). However, it is not as effective for healing as the full 12-position treatment.

The 12-position treatment is recommended as the core treatment when you begin practising Reiki simply because it is the most comprehensive of the three techniques described in this book. From here you can experiment with chakra balancing to observe the differences in outcome and slowly develop your own treatment routine and preference. Likewise, Reiki first aid is helpful for specific physical ailments or for temporary relief, but it also needs to be followed up with the 12-position treatment.

Always remember that Reiki is cumulative and, as a result, the more you do the better it gets. It is also a continuous process; there will never be a day when you are either 'fixed' or 'full'. We need refuelling every day, so Reiki is an important daily routine to establish.

Chapter 10

Treating Animals and Plants

"Our task must be to free ourselves...
by widening our circle of compassion
to embrace all living creatures and
the whole of nature and its beauty."

Albert Einstein

Treating animals

Animals are also wonderful Reiki candidates and tend to respond much like children (I know several vets who will attest to this!). Many animals will move close to you as if they can sense your healing hands, and move away from you when they have had enough. I have had many cats and dogs sitting in my lap with the owner looking on in disbelief saying 'my pet never does that to strangers'. When giving Reiki to animals, simply be open to their movement and place your hands where it feels right. In general the animal will move its body so that your hands are in the right spot and you can simply relax and let the animal dictate the positions and timing.

When we collected feedback from respondents in The Reiki Centre Survey there were so many lovely animal stories.

"My dog got cancer in his stomach when he was less than one year old: the vet had never seen such a young dog get stomach cancer. He told us that there was nothing he could do and that our dog would probably die very young. My mother and I have Reiki and we started healing him. He loved it when we held our hands on his stomach, which we would do for over an hour a day. A couple of months later the vet suggested that our dog took the test one more time. The test came back negative, and the vet declared that the first test must have been wrong. But my mother and I knew that we had healed our dog. He was happy again, he was eating his food again and he wanted to play again." Rosita

"Some friends asked me to do Reiki on one of their horses, Reggae. They had recently had to have another horse put down and Reggae was depressed. He was not eating and he did not look well. He had suffered a back injury many years ago and you could see his back was sagging a bit. I had never done Reiki on a horse before and was a bit nervous. I started Reiki on Reggae's head and he promptly laid it on my shoulder and fell asleep. I moved around doing Reiki in several different places. He let me know when he had received all he wanted and moved away. My friends and I immediately noticed that his back was straighter and he just looked better. His appetite picked up and since that one Reiki treatment he has been doing great." Kelley

"My Siamese cat had kidney failure, so I gave him Reiki every morning. He lived his life without pain, continuing to eat and use the litter box. When the vet checked him he said he could not feel his kidneys, they had shrivelled so much, and he was surprised he could still use the litter box. I gave him Reiki for over seven months." Celeste

"A woman brought her eight-year-old Golden Retriever to me on the recommendation of her veterinarian. The dog had a skin infection, together with unexplained lameness and trembling. After just one session of Reiki, the dog's coat was glossy and shiny. The trembling completely disappeared and never returned." Debra

"I became a Reiki practitioner thanks to a young horse I bought at a local auction. After I'd watched and worked with him, I came to the conclusion he had been abused, even beaten. His hearing and vision are a bit compromised on one side and his hips really bother him sometimes. He used to be terribly afraid of everything! I decided to take Reiki Level One to see if it would help him. He quickly fell in love with his Reiki sessions. Sometimes he lies down, sometimes he takes a nap and sometimes he walks up to me and lays his head in my hands. He has calmed down immensely. Even the farrier has been blown away at how calm he has become, saying, "If I didn't know any better, I'd think this was a different horse!" That is only one example of how much he has changed for the better; fortunately for both of us there are many more." Julie

Treating plants

Plants have a purity of energy that makes them very good for experiments. Plants do not have belief systems and do not have intentions or 'psychological hang-ups'; as a result you can trust that any results you get are not placebo. I have run several experiments with rice, apples, seedlings and cuttings and I encourage you to do the same as it's not only fun but also quite humbling when you see in full the effect the Reiki energy has on living systems. As a general rule of thumb, whatever you Reiki will last longer and show much less sign of decay than the control.

Rice experiment
1. Boil up rice in a pot
2. Use boiling water to sterilize two identical glass jars with tight fitting lids
3. When both jars are completely dry, add a few scoops of the cooked rice into each jar and close the lid tightly
4. Label one jar 'Control' and leave it alone for the entire experiment

5. Label the second jar 'Reiki' and apply Reiki to the jar for five minutes every other day (or daily). You can hover your hands over or around the jar to ensure your body temperature does not affect the experiment
6. Leave the two jars near each other, but at least ten inches apart (to ensure the Reiki cannot affect the 'control')
7. It may take up to a month to see significant results.

Fruit experiment

1. Cut a piece of raw fruit in half
2. Using boiling water, sterilize two identical glass jars with tight fitting lids
3. When both jars are completely dry, add half the fruit into each jar and close the lid tightly
4. Label one jar 'Control' and leave it alone for the entire experiment
5. Label the second jar 'Reiki' and apply Reiki to the jar for five minutes every other day (or daily). You can hover your hands over or around the jar to ensure your body temperature does not affect the experiment
6. Leave the two jars near each other, but at least ten inches apart (to ensure the Reiki cannot affect the 'control')
7. It may take up to two weeks to see significant results.

Flower cuttings

1. Take a bunch of flowers, divide the bunch in half and place in similar vases
2. Reiki the water in one vase for just five minutes, leave the other one untouched
3. See which bunch lasts longer.

When treating plants the recommendation is either to Reiki the roots of the plant, holding the pot or, alternatively, Reiki the water in the watering can to energise it before watering your plants. I have also given Reiki to enormous trees by holding the trunk. As with all living things, however, true health comes from being well looked-after. Reiki will not replace insufficient light, food or water.

Chapter 11

Next Steps

"At the center of your being
you have the answer; you know
who you are and you know what
you want."

Lao Tzu

This book has been written for the beginner and Level One practitioner as an opening to a deeper understanding of what Reiki is and how it can help us to heal. Once you have embarked on your Reiki journey, you may feel inclined to move on and train to a higher level, or even to become a teacher yourself. Although the higher levels of Reiki still access the same Reiki qualities, the tools available also allow for some big differences that bear discussing.

The benefits of higher level training

One of the more surprising findings of The Reiki Centre Survey was the significant improvement in benefits perceived by respondents with higher levels of Reiki training. This is something I was not expecting when I ran the data, though on reflection it makes sense. Reiki Level Two is a quantum leap in many ways, as it takes self-healing to a higher and more deliberate level.

At Reiki Level One we are simply acting as funnels. Reiki flows through our hands and into our cells, where it is used, as it is needed. Of course, we must also take responsibility for making significant changes happen, but essentially, when it comes to the Reiki energy, our conscious minds (or egos) are not in charge and we have no say in what areas are healed, at what rate, and with what priority.

Taking my sciatica as an example: although I saw many emotional improvements during my early months of practising self-Reiki, my back continued to be painful for two more years. This confused me at the time, and I wondered why my back was not healing faster; but eventually I came to realize that I had to release stress and negative thought patterns before my back would heal totally. Reiki at Level One is akin to peeling an onion; you cannot get to the heart of the onion until you have carefully peeled back all the other layers. In this sense the process is safe, natural and gentle. We get exactly what we need and at a rate we can handle.

Usui Reiki Level Two

Reiki Level Two is fundamentally different as it allows us to direct Reiki down a specific pathway. This may seem to contradict what has been said earlier in the book – that Reiki is osmotic and so goes where it is most needed – but it is not. When we are attuned at Level One, Reiki flows along sub-conscious pathways dictated by our body's needs, but after the Level Two attunement we become more conscious about our healing, and thus more involved. We can decide which areas of our lives we want to direct more energy to, be it physical, mental, emotional, or even a specific event or trauma. On many levels, this advanced training takes us much further, much faster. It allows us to decide which layer of the onion we want to peel first, and often results in the dissolution of the layers above, so healing can take place via 'short cuts'.

Reiki Level Two should be taken some time after Level One. In my teaching tradition, a minimum of two months is stipulated between the courses, and this period is an important opportunity to practice Reiki and ensure your energy is high. It is also an important time for self-healing to ensure you are ready to use the Level Two tools wisely. As we become able to choose what we work on, we can sometimes create more chaos if we work on too many different issues all at once!

As with Level One training, there is an enormous discrepancy in the way the classes are taught. I frequently get calls from Level Two practitioners who have little knowledge of the tools at their disposal. Having been taught nothing, they end up with nothing. This level should be full of possibilities and magic, I am hard pushed to cram all the information and tips into ten hours of teaching and would seriously question the effectiveness of a class of less than six hours duration. Many classes seem to focus on the distance healing aspect of Reiki Level Two, but this is only one of many, many applications of Reiki available at this level.

During my Level Two course, a Level Two attunement is given and three symbols are taught. The word 'symbol' often conjures up mystical images of strange cults and suchlike, but in Reiki we use symbols as 'shortcuts' and focussing tools. The Reiki practitioner is then able to use the symbols to enhance their Reiki flow, and to develop alternative uses of the Reiki energy as described below.

The *Empowerment* symbol 'spirals' the energy to maximise Reiki flow rate and power, rather like pressing your thumb on the garden hose to increase its force. It can also be used to un-block areas, specifically chakras. The Empowerment symbol empowers other energy fields as well, such as food and water, crystals and others.

The *Harmony* symbol allows Reiki to be 'wrapped' around other energy fields and environments to increase harmony in, for example, homes, other people, and incidents. The symbol is also used to increase communicative ability, creativity and intuition.

The *Sending* symbol. Like an International Direct Dial number, this symbol allows Reiki to be sent to people in different geographical locations, but also to incidents and events, internal blocks or emotional issues. This is a very powerful source of personal growth as the practitioner can directly tune into issues and fix them at a deep level. This has the effect of melting our icebergs from the inside out and so can often have much quicker and more powerful results than Level One Reiki.

Other healing treatments are taught during a Level Two course, including a powerful chakra balancing treatment, a calming treatment for intense emotional or panic attacks, and a self-treatment which effectively combines the Level One treatment with 'sending' to form a 'turbo' treatment. Level Two training is possibly the minimum standard recommended for those practitioners interested in becoming professional Reiki therapists.

Usui Reiki Level Three

Reiki Level Three is equivalent to Master Training and is often divided into separate courses or sections. In my tradition, Master Training is carried out in two sections, Level 3a (a three-day course) and Masters or Level 3b (an eight- to ten-month, part-time, assignment-based programme). Reiki Level Three is a very transformational programme with the wonderful benefit of being able to pass on Usui Reiki to others. Level Three unlocks all the secrets of Reiki but is also about personal mastery. During the training, students are expected to come up with their own teaching point of view and it can be a time of powerful personal growth.

When the Level Three course is completed, the student becomes a Reiki Master and can go on to train others up to Master level.

Conclusion

"It's getting better all the time"

The Beatles

By stripping Reiki down to its pure and simple basics, I hope this book will provide you with the information (and inspiration) you need to launch your own journey of discovery into the wonderful world of Reiki energy healing.

Do not be afraid to experiment with it. Do not be put off by the myths, superstitions, rules, do's and don'ts that you will no doubt come across along the way. Look at every new piece of information and see if it rings true for you. Trust in your instinct. When you do, you are listening to your balanced, whole self and you will know that the Reiki has done its work.

In summary, it is worth revisiting the qualities that make Reiki so unique and so accessible to us all:

Reiki energy is osmotic: Reiki energy flows as if by osmosis and once it enters the body it will be used where it is most required.

Reiki energy is all-encompassing: It works on all levels: physical, mental and emotional. 'One size fits all' due to the neutral or inert state of the energy as it enters the body. The energy is *used by* the body and does not *act on* the body.

Reiki energy flows automatically: Using our hands as energy funnels, Reiki will 'switch' itself on or off with no personal effort, no skill, or special gift required by us. Anyone can be attuned to Reiki.

Reiki energy is complementary: Due to its inert quality, Reiki is complementary with any other form of healing or medication. There are no known contra-indications.

Reiki energy is universal and limitless: Reiki does not use up personal energy or drain you in any way. Neither does it rely on your state of health. People who are already very sick can use Reiki to treat themselves or others.

When we practice Reiki we are tapping into the purest form of energy available to us: Universal Life Energy. We have free access to this energy and a 'refuel' button that just requires us to lay hands on ourselves or others and relax. Seriously, what could be easier?

All the wisdom we need, all the peace we seek, all the happiness we crave, is just a Reiki treatment away. We just have to *flick the switch* and let our bodies and minds reset to see the peace, calm and balance that is already within us.

Resources
and Notes

[1] The Reiki Centre Pte Ltd, founded by Elaine Grundy in 2007. www.reikicentre.com.sg.

[2] USA Today *"More hospitals offer alternative therapies for mind, body, spirit"*, 15 September 2008.

[3] Frank Arjava Petter, *Reiki Fire: New Information about the Origins of the Reiki Power: A Complete Manual.* Shangri-La.

[4] Frank Arjava Petter, *Reiki–The Legacy of Dr. Usui* and *The Hayashi Reiki Manual: Traditionjal Japanese Healing Techniques from the Founder of the Western Reiki System.* Shangri-La.

[5] Webster's New Collegiate Dictionary. Springfied MA: G & C Merriam Company; 1979; 1230.

[6] Annals of Family Medicine. 2005;3(3):255-262.

[7] Suzanne C. Segerstrom and Gregory E. Miller, *Psychological Stress and the Human Immune System: A Meta-Analytic Study of 30 Years of Inquiry.* Psychological Bulletin, Vol 130(4), Jul 2004, 601-630.

[8] Norman Doidge, *The Brain That Changes Itself.* James H. Silberman Books. (An excellent summary and the latest research on the way the brain hardwires.)

[9] Osho, *The Man who loved seagulls.* St Martin's Griffin. p. 12.

[10] Jill Bolte Taylor Ph.D., *My stroke of insight.* Penguin Group. p. 153.

[11] Elaine Grundy, The Reiki Centre *Survey.* www.reikireport.com. p. 21.

[12] Science Daily, *Brain Waves and Meditation.* March 31, 2010. http://www.sciencedaily.com/releases/2010/03/100319210631.htm.

[13] Shulman RG, Rothman DL, Behar KL, Hyder F., *Energetic basis of brain activity: implications for neuroimaging.* Trends in Neuroscience. 2004 Aug (8): 489-95.

[14] Andrew Newberg, Eugene D'Aquili, Vince Rause, *Why God Won't Go Away.* Ballantine Books.

[15] Andrew Newberg, Mark Robert Waldman, *How God Changes our Mind.* Ballantine Books. p. 27.

[16] Elaine Grundy, *The Reiki Centre Survey.* www.reikireport.com. p. 35 and 38.

[17] Ibid p. 29.

[18] Ibid p. 30.

[19] Bruce H. Lipton PhD, *The Biology of Belief.* Hay House, Inc. p. 95.

[20] Hermann Nabi et al., *Low Pessimism Protects Against Stroke: The Health and Social Support (HeSSup) Prospective Cohort Study.* American Heart Association, Inc. 2010; 41: 187-190.

[21] Marty S Player et al., *Psychosocial Factors Predict Hypertension and Coronary Heart Disease*, Annals of Family Medicine. 2007 (5) 403-411.

[22] Time Magazine, *Faith and Healing.* 24 June 1996.

[23] Frank Arjava Petter, *Reiki Fire: New Information about the Origins of the Reiki Power: A Complete Manual.* Shangri-La. p. 30.

[24] Walter Lubeck, Frank Arjava Petter, William Lee Rand, *The Spirit of Reiki.* Shangri-La. p. 153.

Reiki Music CDs

My long-time friend, Peter Forster, has composed some wonderful music to accompany your Reiki treatments. His two CDs, *Sadhana* and *Homecoming*, are available at *the Reiki Centre* or directly from Peter. Order from:

www.reikicentre.com.sg

www.soulssong.com

Appendix:

The Reiki Centre Survey Topline Findings

1. Summary

This survey quantifies aspects of Reiki that have been reported anecdotally by Reiki practitioners over the years. It helps to provide deeper understanding of how the benefits of Reiki are experienced. Of particular focus is the aspect of self-treatment, termed 'self-Reiki' in this report.

1.1 Aims of the survey

The first aim was to identify areas of wellness that respond best to Reiki, be they physical, lifestyle or emotional/mental elements. The second aim was to more deeply understand the key criteria for successfully utilizing Reiki to provide the maximum benefits.

1.2 Key findings

a. Areas of wellness that respond best to Reiki are emotional/ mental elements; specifically increased feelings of content-ment, peace, self-love, and happiness; as well as a decrease in negative emotional states such as stress, anxiety, and anger.

b. The key criteria for successfully utilizing Reiki is the amount of self-Reiki administered. Reiki is a cumulative therapy; the more hours of self-Reiki the respondent does, the better the results they report.

1.3 Methodology

The survey went online from January 16th 2010 to March 31st 2010. A total of 546 respondents completed the survey. All responses

were collected using the online software provided by www.
surveymonkey.com. Survey requests were sent to Reiki Masters
asking them to disseminate the information to their students and
postings linking to the survey were made on Reiki-related sites,
newsletters and social media networks.

This survey was designed to gather personal perceptions and
experiences in order to help quantify the benefits of Reiki. To
measure the level of improvement perceived, questions relating to
the three areas of wellness detailed below were answered using a
five-point scale:

1. **General or lifestyle** – for example:
   - Overall wellness
   - Diet & nutrition
   - Exercise
   - Sleep quality
   - Smoking

2. **Physical ailments and issues** – for example:
   - Muscle Pain/cramp
   - Back pain/ problems
   - Headaches/migraines
   - Colds/flu
   - Allergies

3. **Mental/emotional well-being** – for example:
   - Anger
   - Anxiety/ worry
   - Stress
   - Self-love
   - Peace
   - Contentment

1.4 Demographics

Please note this survey is not a representative sample of global Reiki
practitioners.

47% of respondents are trained to Level Three or Master, 32%
are Level Two and 21% are Level One. Half of the respondents

have been practicing Reiki for less than four years. The majority of respondents practice from one to six hours of Reiki per week (62%). 19% practice over seven hours per week and 19% less than an hour per week. The majority of respondents are within the 31 to 60 age range. 83% are female.

Respondents come mainly from Europe and North America but over 20 countries were represented overall. The questionnaire was only available in English and German.

1.5 Identified areas of wellness that respond best to Reiki
Results are seen over a wide variety of measures. Most significantly in the area of mental/emotional wellness, followed by physical wellness and finally in areas of lifestyle. See Chart 1.5 below.

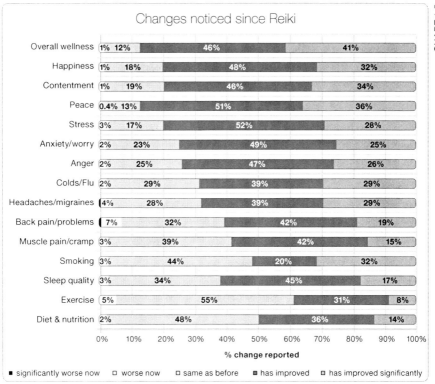

CHART 1.5

a. Overwhelmingly, respondents notice improvements in overall mental well-being which they describe as calm, peace, self-love, and connectedness. Many notice a decrease in negative emotional states such as stress, anxiety, and anger. These improvements happen quickly (within one year of practicing Reiki) and continue to cumulate.

b. With physical ailments (such as colds, migraines, back pain and pain), respondents reported a wide range of success but these aspects appear more arbitrary in results. The physical improvements in health appear to be linked more closely to the amount of self-Reiki the respondent does, i.e. the more respondents self-Reiki, the better the results achieved.

c. Lifestyle improvements (for example changes in habits such as smoking, sleep, exercise and dietary improvements) are the most arbitrary and ill defined of all the measures and appear to have an impact for some, and not others. These aspects play only a minor role in the findings of this report.

1.6 The key success criteria for utilizing Reiki

a. Findings show that Reiki is a cumulative therapy; the more hours of self-Reiki the respondent does, the better the results they report. Respondents who report doing self-Reiki daily (seven or more hours per week) achieve on average three times the perceived benefits of a respondent doing self-Reiki for less than one hour per week. Overall the respondents using Reiki for less than one hour per week are much less likely to notice any change.

Chart 1.6a illustrates this by looking at one of the measurements, 'Overall Wellness', and plots results by number of hours of self-Reiki per week. There is a clear correlation between number of hours and level of significant improvement perceived by respondents.

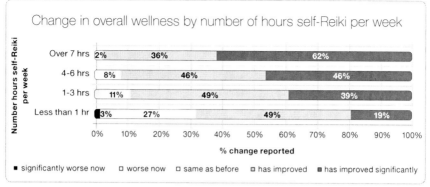

CHART 1.6A

b. Reiki continues to provide benefits over time; the longer the respondent has been practicing Reiki, the better the results reported. Respondents who have just started practicing Reiki (less than one year) have an average 50/50 chance of seeing an improvement compared with a 70/20 chance if they have been practicing Reiki for over seven years.

However, the number of hours of self-Reiki per week has a powerful impact, Respondents practicing more self-Reiki notice improvements more quickly. We can hypothesize that doing more hours of self-Reiki can shorten the number of years to achieving significant results, as seen in Chart 1.6b. Due to the sample size, we have combined the hours of usage into two categories: 'less than four hours', and 'over four hours'.

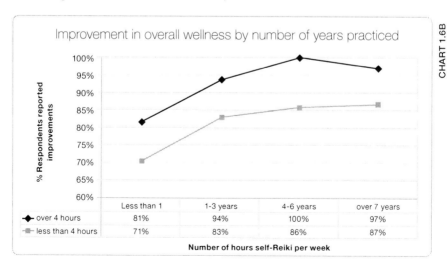

CHART 1.6B

Note the high level of improvement noted by all respondents (over 70% in all categories noticed an improvement in overall wellness).

c. Other areas of high reported improvements included self-love, peace, and contentment (more than 70% of light users – respondents doing self-Reiki less than four hours per week – who had practiced Reiki for less than one year noticed improvements). Chart 1.6c illustrates this finding. Note the high reported improvements continue to rise with time. Heavy users reported even higher percentage improvements.

This finding indicates that even moderate levels of self-Reiki can be beneficial for increasing these positive feelings.

The level of training does have some bearing on the results; in general the higher the level of training in Reiki, the better the results, but only when comparing similar numbers of hours of self-Reiki practiced. A Reiki Master will not necessarily get better results than a Level One trained respondent if the Level One respondent does more hours of self-Reiki per week, as chart 1.6d illustrates.

CHART 1.6C

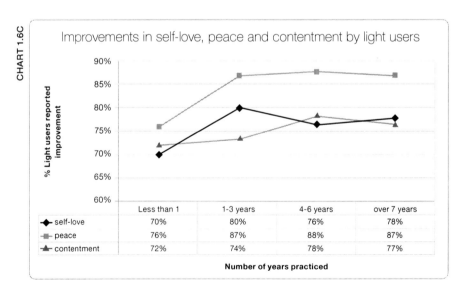

Improvements in self-love, peace and contentment by light users

% Light users reported improvement

	Less than 1	1-3 years	4-6 years	over 7 years
self-love	70%	80%	76%	78%
peace	76%	87%	88%	87%
contentment	72%	74%	78%	77%

Number of years practiced

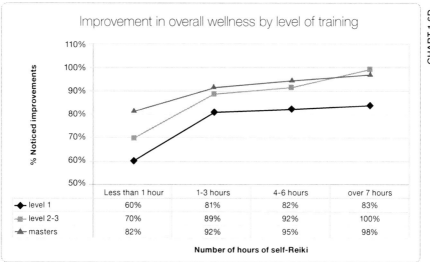

CHART 1.6D

Improvement in overall wellness by level of training

Number of hours of self-Reiki	Less than 1 hour	1-3 hours	4-6 hours	over 7 hours
level 1	60%	81%	82%	83%
level 2-3	70%	89%	92%	100%
masters	82%	92%	95%	98%

2. Further Recommendations

The results show unequivocally that the majority of respondents benefit from self-Reiki, most specifically for enhanced peace, calm and balance.

When further studying the effects of Reiki and when presenting Reiki to the medical profession, or when designing clinical trials, it is important to bear in mind the key findings of this survey. Reiki is not primarily a 'quick fix' and the most beneficial results are seen after many hours of self-Reiki. Further research needs to take into account the many hours of treatment required before meaningful measurements can be taken, and should bear in mind that the overwhelming benefits people derive from Reiki are not medically oriented, but are related to feelings of wellbeing, relaxation and calm.

Reiki could be likened to meditation in terms of its cumulative and long term benefits, and the recommendations of this report is that future research should track Reiki benefits over time, specifically monitoring stress-related measures and immunity.

For detailed findings: **www.reikireport.com**

About the Author

Elaine has been teaching Reiki for over 15 years, starting her training in Hong Kong and then teaching around the world in the UK, Portugal, USA, Malaysia and Singapore.

She spent over ten years in the corporate world, working in advertising and market research before setting up her own training and coaching consultancy, specialising in leadership and communication, in 1999.

For years she has balanced her corporate life with a deep respect and love of spiritual teachings. She believes that success in our modern world needs to balance and combine both outer Doing and inner Being. Then life really becomes joyful and fun!

She trained with Dr John Veltheim, graduating as a Reiki Master in 1995, and in 2008 she completed Kundalini Reiki training with Janet Bowden and Ole Gabrielsen. Elaine trained with CoachU in 2000 and specialized in 'Law of Attraction' coaching in 2004 after a year-long programme with Eva Gregory in the USA. Recently she completed the School for The Work, with Byron Katie.

Elaine now dedicates her time to teaching Reiki, to life and personal coaching, and to her two little princesses.

About the Reiki Centre

The Reiki Centre Pte Ltd was established in Singapore in 2007 to provide a space for Reiki workshops, healing and community. The Centre provides a range of services including meditation, yoga and self-development classes to enable people to find their balance.

www.reikicentre.com.sg

CPSIA information can be obtained at www.ICGtesting.com
Printed in the USA
BVOW031306100112

280224BV00010B/135/P